Practical
Technical Writing

Ritchie R. Ward

CONSULTING EDITOR | **R. M. Ohmann**

Practical Technical Writing

ALFRED·A·KNOPF | *New York*

TO **Bill**

Preface

THIS BOOK IS A PRACTICAL GUIDE TO THE PRINCIPLES OF TECHNICAL writing for students of engineering and the natural sciences—including agriculture, architecture, industrial management, forestry, public health—and some of the behavioral sciences. The treatment is sufficiently broad to meet the requirements of undergraduate classes, as well as to supplement graduate seminar courses leading to the writing of masters' theses and doctoral dissertations. The many examples of published writing quoted and the detailed criticisms of them will also provide the individual student with a reference suitable for independent study.

Present-day engineers and scientists working in industry and government need no reminder that professional advancement is increasingly dependent on their skills in preparing technical memorandums, reports, and papers for publication in professional journals. This book is also for them, to be used either as a text for in-plant seminar courses or as a handbook for independent study and reference.

The author writes from a background of more than three decades in industrial research and has written, coauthored, or edited technical memorandums and reports numbering in the hundreds. He has also taught courses in technical writing for college undergraduates, graduate students, and technicians, engineers, and scientists in both industry and government.

In preparing this book, the author has drawn extensively on the work of many scholars of the English language, including Ralph M. Albaugh, Sheridan Baker, Cleanth Brooks, Mason Cooley, D. W. Emery, H. A. Gleason, Jr., John Halverson, Baxter Hathaway, Archibald A. Hill, J. N. Hook, Sumner Ives, John E. Jordan, Thomas S. Kane, Harold C. Martin, Richard M. Ohmann, R. W. Pence, Leonard J. Peters, Charles Child Walcutt, Robert Penn Warren, Hulon Willis, and in particular, Walter S. Campbell, late director of courses in professional writing at the University of Oklahoma.

Herbert Jacobs, of the Department of Journalism at the University of California, Berkeley, read many of the early drafts of the manuscript, and his perceptive and helpful criticisms are gratefully acknowledged. For the illustrations in Chapter 1, which show how a research man can suit his writing style to his reader, whether that reader be an intensive specialist, a reader of the *Saturday Evening Post,* or a high school student, the author is indebted to Frank A. Brown, Jr., Morrison Professor of Biology at Northwestern University.

It is asking much of any wife to live at once with a man and a book, but this author's did both, besides contributing shrewd commentary on the sense and sensibility of the work.

Orinda, California   R. R. W.

Contents

PART 4 **Appendix**

Pieces for Analysis, 221

PART 1

Your Reader

1 | Three Keys to Effective Writing

Every scientist and engineer needs three keys to effective writing. Before the technical writer puts a word on paper, he should:

- Know his reader
- Know his purpose
- Know his subject

Does this sound oversimplified? Perhaps so. Yet the melancholy fact is that most poor technical reports *are* poor because their writers neglected one or more of these principles. Too bad—these writers made their jobs far too hard.

This chapter and the next discuss the elements of the writer's relation to his reader. Just as the archer takes the most careful aim before he releases his arrow, so should the technical writer pinpoint his audience before he lets fly with words. You must write for a real reader. You cannot write blind—as in a vacuum.

Almost always, the first question will be: What level of technical sophistication does *this* audience have?

In talking to a colleague, a mechanical engineer will use highly technical terms to discuss ammonia as a fuel for spark ignition engines—and then shift gears smoothly to explain the same idea to his son in junior high school.

Colonel John Glenn would use space jargon that a layman could not grasp in talking to fellow astronauts. But when he described the first American orbital space flight before a joint session of Congress, he said:

There seemed to be little sensation of speed although the craft was traveling at about five miles per second—a speed that I, too, find difficult to comprehend . . . The view from that altitude defies description.

I had listened earlier to Alan and Gus both describe this and was eagerly looking forward to it, and in their wildest use of adjectives, they didn't describe what it's like even.

Nor can I describe it.

The horizon colors are brilliant and the sunsets are very spectacular. And it's hard to beat a day in which you're permitted the luxury of seeing four sunsets.[1]

Note how naturally Colonel Glenn adapted his report to the technical level of his audience.

The General Audience

For perspective, let us first look at the whole population of persons interested in learning more about science and engineering. They extend over a wide range of age, education, and experience. A young mother wants to know more about measles; a research director needs the latest word on high-temperature ceramics; a student wants career information about bioengineering. The list goes on and on.

Must a single writer learn to meet the needs of all such

[1] *Congressional Record,* February 26, 1962.

audiences? Usually not. But it is quite possible: a single hand can write in various ways.

Watch what happens when a university research professor—a world authority in a highly abstruse field—aims his pen at five different audiences. They are the readers of the following periodicals:

Periodical	Circulation	Readership
Physiological Zoology	850	Superspecialists
Biological Bulletin	1,500	Marine biologists
Science	100,000	Most scientists
Scientific American	370,000	Intelligent laymen
Saturday Evening Post	6,600,000	Anybody

The titles and circulation figures[2] of these periodicals tell us much about their audiences. *Physiological Zoology* deals with matters so abstruse that the journal goes to fewer than a thousand superspecialists worldwide. *Biological Bulletin* is chiefly of interest to marine biologists. *Science* takes in all the sciences and is also read by some engineers. *Scientific American* interests intelligent men everywhere: attorneys, accountants, educators, insurance men, preachers, and brokers. Finally, *Saturday Evening Post* goes into homes by the millions and is read by family members spanning three generations; many of these have never gone to college.

Readers of technical information may therefore range from a handful of specialists to millions of almost anybody. The point to keep in mind is that a skilled writer can adjust his presentation to meet the needs of many different audiences. The following selections will make this clear. Read them carefully, for in the next chapter we use them to show how level of reading difficulty can be tested objectively.

I

Recent studies have provided reasons to postulate that the primary timer for long-cycle biological rhythms that are closely similar in period to the natural geophysical ones and that persist in so-called constant conditions is, in fact, one of organismic response to subtle geophysical fluctuations which pervade ordinary constant conditions in the laboratory. In such constant laboratory conditions a wide variety

2 *Standard Periodicals Directory* (New York: Oxbridge, 1964–1965).

of organisms have been demonstrated to display, nearly equally con-
spicuously, metabolic periodicities of both solar-day and lunar-day
frequencies, with their interference derivative, the 29.5-day synodic
month, and in some instances even the year. These metabolic cycles
exhibit day-by-day irregularities and distortions which have been established to be highly significantly correlated with aperiodic meteoro-
logical and other geophysical changes.[3]

II

The question of whether living things are sensitive to terrestrial mag-
netism has undoubtedly fleeted through the minds of innumerable
persons since this geophysical factor first became known. But neither
the naturalist, observing the behavior of organisms in the field during
their continuing responses to the myriads of more obvious physical
factors, nor the experimental biologist, casually testing the response
of living things to artificial magnetic fields, even very strong ones,
found any consistent evidence that living creatures perceived this
weak terrestrial force. It is a common observation that animals in
nature may come to bear at any given moment apparently all possible compass relations in their bodily orientation; orientation of the
normal resting or foraging animal to the horizontal component of
the magnetic field would be expected generally to be of no adaptive
significance.[4]

III

Familiar to all are the rhythmic changes in innumerable processes
of animals and plants in nature. Examples of phenomena geared to the
24-hour solar day produced by rotation of the earth relative to the
sun are sleep movements of plant leaves and petals, spontaneous
activity in numerous animals, emergence of flies from their pupal cases,
color changes of the skin in crabs, and wakefulness in man. Sample
patterns of daily fluctuations, each interpretable as adaptive for the
species are illustrated in the figure. Rhythmic phenomena linked to the
24-hour and 50-minute lunar-day period of rotation of the earth relative to the moon are most conspicuous among intertidal organisms
whose lives are dominated by the ebb and flow of the ocean tides.[5]

[3] Emma D. Terracini and Frank A. Brown, Jr., "Periodisms in Mouse
'Spontaneous' Activity Synchronized with Major Geophysical Cycles," *Physiological Zoology*, XXV (January, 1962), 27–37.

[4] Frank A. Brown, Jr., "Responses of the Planarian, Dugesia, and the Protozoan, Paramecium, to Very Weak Horizontal Magnetic Fields," *Biological
Bulletin*, 123 (October, 1962), 264–281.

[5] Frank A. Brown, Jr., "Living Clocks," *Science*, 130 (December 4, 1959),
1535–1544.

I V

Everyone knows that there are individuals who are able to awaken morning after morning at the same time within a few minutes. Are they awakened by sensory cues received unconsciously, or is there some "biological clock" that keeps accurate account of the passage of time? Students of the behavior of animals in relation to their environment have long been interested in the biological clock question.

Most animals show a rhythmic behavior pattern of one sort or another. For instance, many animals that live along the ocean shores have behavior cycles which are repeated with the ebb and flow of the tides, each cycle averaging about 12½ hours in length.[6]

V

One of the greatest riddles of the universe is the uncanny ability of living things to carry out their normal activities with clocklike precision at a particular time of the day, month, and year. Why do oysters plucked from a Connecticut bay and shipped to a Midwest laboratory continue to time their lives to ocean tides 800 miles away? How do potatoes in hermetically sealed containers predict atmospheric pressure trends two days in advance? What effects do the lunar and solar rhythms have on the life habits of man? Living things clearly possess powerful adaptive capacities—but the explanation of whatever strange and permeative forces are concerned continues to challenge science.[7]

Obviously, each of these pieces is about living clocks. But what a difference in treatment! By careful attention to the needs of each audience, Dr. Brown, who is Morrison Professor of Biology at Northwestern University, was able to adjust his writing for a coterie of 850 or for a mass audience of 6.6 million.

Then, too, scientists and engineers are often asked to explain their specialties to high school students, for example. These are rewarding assignments, but tough. Here is how Dr. Brown handled one of them.

V I

At almost exactly the same time as last evening, just as the twilight was deepening, you became aware of a faint murmur in the grass somewhere below the bushes near the water's edge. All along the lake

6 Frank A. Brown, Jr., "Biological Clocks and the Fiddler Crab," *Scientific American,* 190 (April, 1954), 34–37.

7 Frank A. Brown, Jr., "Life's Mysterious Clocks," *Saturday Evening Post,* 233 (December 24, 1960), 18–19.

shore something seemed to be waking and stirring. The murmur quickly grew to a low, audible drone and, within minutes, increased strikingly in volume, so that it soon sounded like a waterfall. Then slowly a shimmering cloud made of thousands, perhaps even millions, of tiny flies rose from the water's edge and drifted into the surrounding forest like an evening mist.[8]

Perhaps these examples represent extremes. But they have been offered here for two reasons: first, to show, as will be done in the next chapter, how the level of reading difficulty can be adjusted to meet various audience needs; second, to refute an argument that some scientists and engineers give so often that it sounds like a phonograph record: "But surely you can't expect me to report the very complex technical matters with which I deal in the language of children!" This worn-out record belongs in the trash can. The "complexity of subject matter" excuse is mainly humbug. Get a copy of Dr. Brown's little pamphlet *Biological Clocks,* cited above, and read it through. You may be surprised to see how much solid technical information can be put in such easy, simple style.

The Technical Audience

Naturally, the audience for technical reports is far narrower than any general audience interested in scientific and engineering developments. Nevertheless, even within this narrower group, a substantial spread is found in the level of technical sophistication of its members.

Some technical writing may be addressed to a very narrow band of the technical audience spectrum. Brief technical memorandums from one specialist to another are of this sort. Suppose that a plasma engineer wants to report a new wrinkle in operating a plasma generator. If he is addressing other plasma engineers only, he may use whatever technical jargon he wishes. His colleagues will understand.

But as soon as the plasma engineer needs to report to all *electrical* engineers, or to *all* engineers, or to *management,* he must adjust his level of presentation accordingly. Within narrower limits, this is the same process that we showed in operation before:

[8] Frank A. Brown, Jr., *Biological Clocks* (Boston: Heath, 1962), p. 1.

switching from the readership of *Physiological Zoology* to the readership of *Scientific American*.

A further very practical problem faces the technical report writer working in industry or government. Usually he lacks the time to report first to specialists, then to modify his presentation for wider audiences. Things move too fast. One report must meet the needs of all. Attorneys, engineers, accountants, purchasing agents, and corporate officers—all must be able to make decisions based on its facts and conclusions.

This immediately raises a question: What devices does the skilled writer use to take aim at his audience? Knowing the answers will repay the close study suggested in the following chapters.

A glance at the Contents will make clear the plan of the book. Part 1 explains the relationship between the reader and the writer; Part 2 helps the writer to focus on his basic purposes; Part 3 shows many devices for relating subject knowledge to the finished report; and Part 4 contains three models showing how competent craftsmen have used these principles to solve the kinds of problems that face technical writers everywhere. The models are a technical abstract, a book chapter, and a technical report.

Following each of the first five chapters, you will find additional models for study. These have been selected from the published literature with two purposes in view: first, to complement the chapter; and second, to serve as examples of the skillful application of the particular principles discussed in the chapter.

In his courses in professional writing at the University of Oklahoma, the late Walter S. Campbell used to tell his students that the elements of good learning were three: a point of view, a method of work, and enthusiasm. For technical writing, this book presents the point of view and the method of work. The enthusiasm must obviously be your own.

Sounder Thinking
Through Clearer Writing

F. Peter Woodford

Dr. Woodford is an affiliate of the Rockefeller University, New York, N.Y., and executive editor of the Journal of Lipid Research.

IN THE LINKED WORLDS OF EXPERIMENTAL SCIENCE, SCI-
entific editing, and science communication many scientists are
considering just how serious an effect the bad writing in our
journals will have on the future of science.

All are agreed that the articles in our journals—even the
journals with the highest standards—are, by and large, poorly
written. Some of the worst are produced by the kind of author
who consciously pretends to a "scientific scholarly" style. He
takes what should be lively, inspiring, and beautiful and, in
an attempt to make it seem dignified, chokes it to death with

Science, 156 (May, 1967), 743–745; reprinted by permission of the author
and the American Association for the Advancement of Science.

stately abstract nouns; next, in the name of scientific impartiality, he fits it with a complete set of passive constructions to drain away any remaining life's blood or excitement; then he embalms the remains in molasses of polysyllable, wraps the corpse in an impenetrable veil of vogue words, and buries the stiff old mummy with much pomp and circumstance in the most distinguished journal that will take it. Considered either as a piece of scholarly work or as a vehicle of communication, the product is appalling. The question is, Does it matter?

Does the Standard of Writing Matter?

Some editors believe it does, and either work themselves into the ground or employ large staffs to set the writing right. Others regard the correction of an illogical or pompous sentence as tantamount to remodeling the author's thinking, and consequently none of their business. The majority conclude that, if a paper represents sound work and is reasonably intelligible, no lasting damage is done if it is published complete with all its blemishes. The blemishes may include ungrammatical constructions, confused thought, ambiguity, unjustifiable interpretation, subspecialty jargon, concealed hedging, inadequate description of statistical treatment, or imperfect controls.

I disagree with the majority conclusion. I am amazed by the patience with which my colleagues read these blemished scientific articles. I think that the spirit in which articles are often written, in which the object seems to be to impress the reader rather than express an idea, is all wrong. I think that we should protest vigorously about poor writing in scientific articles when it occurs, and *not* be indulgent about it. And I think we should take steps to ensure that the standard of scientific writing goes up. I feel strongly enough about it to teach a course on the Principles of Scientific Writing for graduate students, in the hope that when they come to contribute to the literature they will do a better job than we, the scientists of today, seem to have done.

Sometimes a skeptic will ask me, "Do you really think it's so important to improve scientific writing? We know it's usually a bit on the pompous side, but once you get used to the conventions you can zip through it pretty easily and get to the author's meaning." Personally, I *don't* find it so easy to zip through the pretentious constructions, and I think that one all too frequently arrives at a meaning that was not intended. But more telling than either of these reasons for concern is this: I have definite and clear-cut evidence that the scientific writing in our journals exerts a corrupting influence on young scientists—on their writing, their reading, and their thinking.

Decline of Writing, Reading, and Thinking

When science students enter graduate school they often write with admirable directness and clarity of purpose, like this:

In order to determine the molecular size and shape of A and B, I measured their sedimentation and diffusion constants. The results are given in Table 1. They show that A is a roughly spherical molecule of molecular weight 36,000. The molecular weight of B remains uncertain since the sample seems to be impure. This is being further investigated.

Two years later, these same students' writing is verbose, pompous, full of fashionable circumlocutions as well as dangling constructions, and painfully polysyllabic, like this:

In order to evaluate the possible significance of certain molecular parameters at the subcellular level, and to shed light on the conceivable role of structure configuration in spatial relationships of intracellular macromolecules, an integrated approach [see *1*] to the problem of cell diffusivity has been devised and developed. The results, which are in a preliminary stage, are discussed here in some detail because of their possible implication in mechanisms of diffusivity in a wider sphere.

The student can no longer write: he pontificates.

What has brought about the change? Clearly, the students have copied these dreary and pretentious phrases from the scientific literature. They have been dutifully studying it, as they are urged to do, and it has warped their style to the point that they can no longer walk to the door without "utilizing a pedestrian relocation," or sip their coffee without "prior elevation of the containing vessel to facilitate imbibition."

Concomitantly, something drastic happens to their powers of reading. As one of the assignments in my course, my students had to write an abstract of a published paper. The paper itself was brief, simple, and well written. I was dismayed to find that at least half of my students misread the paper in three major ways. First, they referred to 20-day-old rats, although the age of the animals was never given—the article described 20-gram rats; second, they talked about specific activity of the cholesterol injected, whereas the specific activity was never stated—the figure they had got hold of was actually the number of millicuries injected per kilogram of rat body weight, and they had misread it as mc/mg; last, and most amazing of all, they gave conclusions *directly opposite* to those indicated both by the data and by the authors of the article they were abstracting!

Now these students are by no means numskulls—they are like the rest of us, busy scientists zipping quickly through the literature to get to the authors' meaning. This is where the habit of guess-work leads.

Worst of all, there is a deterioration in the quality of students' *thinking* as they study the scientific literature. In a survey paper by one of my best students, everything was going along nicely, and everybody's head was clear, until we fell into the mire of this sentence:

A variety of stimulatory hormones, irrespective of their chemical nature, are characterized by their ability to influence the synthesis of messenger RNA as a prerequisite for the secondary biologic events characteristic of the particular target organ.

"What on earth do you mean by that?" I asked. He blushed, and said, "Actually it's a quotation, I forgot to put in the quotation marks." "Well, but what do you suppose it means, anyway?" He couldn't be absolutely sure. It seemed to clinch his argument, and it *sounded impressive.* And when he told me the name of the journal it came from, my spirits sank. How can we hope to have our students think straight if we can't send them to the most celebrated journal in the country without cautioning them about the woolly thinking they will find there? For I cannot be tolerant, as some people are, and say, "Well, great scientists often write badly." You can't get away from it: execrable writing like this is the product of shoddy thinking, of careless condescension, or of pretentiousness. None of these is good for science.

Bringing about Improvement

These, then, are the negative effects of the scientific literature I have observed in the course of teaching scientific writing. I am glad to say that there are also definite positive findings. The most striking observation is that by teaching writing you can actually strengthen students' ability not only to write but also to read more attentively and to think more logically and rigorously.

It is surely no accident that greater lucidity and accuracy in thinking should result from the study of clarity and precision in writing. For writing necessarily uses *words,* and almost all thinking is done with words. One cannot even decide what to have for dinner, or whether to cross town by bus or taxi, without expressing the alternatives to oneself in words. My experience is, and the point of my whole course is, that the discipline of marshaling words into formal sentences, writing them down, and examining the written statement is bound to clarify thought. Once ideas have been written down, they can be analyzed critically and dispassionately; they can be examined at another time, in another mood, by another expert. Thoughts can therefore be developed, and if they are not precise at the first written formulation, they can be made so at a second attempt.

The power of writing as an aid in thinking is not often appreciated. Everyone knows that someone who writes successfully gets his thoughts completely in order before he publishes. But it is seldom pointed out that the very act of writing can help to clarify thinking. Put down woolly thoughts on paper, and their woolliness is immediately exposed. If students come to realize this, they will write willingly and frequently at all stages of their work, instead of relegating "writing up" to the very end and regarding it as a dreadful chore that has very little to do with their "real" work.

In teaching scientific writing it is not difficult to point out the absurdity of the bombastic phraseology discussed above, and to teach students to simplify their writing and make it direct and vigorous. But these stylistic considerations only scratch the surface of what is really at fault in many scientific articles. I am appalled by the frequent publication of papers that describe most minutely what experiments were done, and how, but with no hint of why, or what they mean. Cast thy data upon the waters, the authors seem to think, and they will come back interpreted.

If this approach to publication is to be successfully thwarted by a course on scientific writing, the course should concentrate primarily on clarifying the students' thoughts about the purpose of a piece of research, the conclusions that can justifiably be drawn, and the significance of those conclusions; matters of style are of subsidiary importance. The course should focus on a method for getting these thoughts fully worked out—the technique of writing them down for critical appraisal. The essence of the approach is: Writing clarifies thought.

Considerations in a Scientific Writing Course

A course on scientific writing is best given, perhaps, within the framework of writing a journal article—for the practical reason that students are familiar with this type of publication and know that they will have to produce journal articles in the course of their work. The most receptive students are those who have done some research and who are therefore psychologically ready to consider how they can best present it in a journal.

These are the kinds of question that should be considered:

"In the work to be described, what was the question asked and what are the answers obtained?" These must be clearly placed before the reader. Students, with their recent results in mind, can often tell you what their *answers* are, but they are not always so sure of what the *question* was. Here is the first opportunity to test the hypothesis that writing clarifies thought. When they write down the questions asked and the answers obtained, students frequently come to see that the answers they have are to questions different from what they had thought. Fortunately, the questions to which they do have the answers are usually valid and important, but the difference from the previous state of affairs is that each student is now able to define the true subject of the paper he is about to write. He will not confuse his readers, or himself, with a paper that does not match its title; on the contrary, he can now commit a fitting title to paper and keep closely to the subject it defines through all the subsequent steps, without wandering off into irrelevancies. In addition, he often perceives what the questions are that he would now *like* to ask, and begins to design experiments to answer them. Writing has clarified thought.

The next questions are, "What was the purpose of the work, and what is the significance of the conclusions?" Purpose and significance should always be stated for the reader. At this point, surprisingly, a storm of protest arises. "The work is descriptive!" the students cry. "The reader who is knowledgeable in the field will grasp the purpose, and draw his own conclusions." They seem to think that in research you don't need to have a clear purpose, or to state the conclusions drawn from your frantic activity; that the technique of Science is to mix A and B, inject C into rats, heat it up, precipitate it, centrifuge it, analyze it—and hope against hope that the results will throw light on some "problem" that has not even been defined. And it's not only raw students who think this: examination of the literature reveals that the attitude is widespread. When, however, the students are made to put the problem *in writing* they see why they did the experiments—and why, perhaps, others would have been more to the point. Their probing into the unknown becomes less haphazard, because it is more disciplined.

Any supervisor of research tries to apply this kind of training, of course. All I would like to do is to systematize the training, and to get writing accepted as a regular part of the apparatus for self-criticism.

Other considerations in a course on scientific writing (2) include methods for separating main issues from side issues and side issues from irrelevancies; the function of publication; methods of search; the nature of scientific proof—essentially, in one guise or another, most of the aspects of scientific method. Lastly, toward the end of such a course, students can be taught to recognize and avoid the sort of clumsy and barbaric sentence constructions with which our literature is strewn. All these points should be made in the name of three things that the budding scientist is bound to have respect for: logic, clarity of thought, and precision.

The process of educating scientists is becoming increasingly complex. The student has to learn more and more facts, study exceedingly complex theories that are out of date before he can master them, and become adept at using more and more machines. We seldom make him, or even let him, write—which is the only way for him to find out if his thoughts are clear or muddled. Surely, the object of a university training is not so much the acquisition of knowledge as the development of the power to think. I believe we can strengthen scientific thinking by teaching scientific writing. If this is so, the teaching of scientific writing should not be, as it is at present, almost entirely neglected, but should be accorded a place at the very heart of a science curriculum.

Much attention is currently being paid to the streamlining and automation of information retrieval and the possible use of computers not merely to compile bibliographies but to enable scientists seated at widely separated consoles to engage in "dialogues." In view of all this it seems, perhaps, slightly old-fashioned to be concerned with precise formulation of thought in written language, composed without haste and considered with care. Yet I am convinced that unless we do concern ourselves with it, unless we do train our students to use the technique of writing to clarify thinking, communication between scientists will degenerate into chaos and scientific thinking will decay into a haze of fruitless intuitive feeling.

Summary

Bad scientific writing involves more than stylistic inelegance: it is often the outward and visible form of an inward confusion of thought. The scientific literature at its present standard distorts rather than forms the graduate student's view of scientific knowledge and thought, and corrupts his ability to write, to read, and to think.

Strong educational measures are needed to effect reform. I advocate a course on scientific writing as an essential feature in every scientist's training. Such a course delves deep into the philosophy and method of science if it deals with logic, precision, and clarity; on how these qualities can be achieved in writing; and on how such achievement strengthens the corresponding faculties in thinking.

References and Notes

1. Whenever an "integrated approach" is mentioned (why anyone should use a disintegrated approach passes all comprehension), the reader should steel himself for other tidbits of Fashionable Foundationese: "constellation of ideas," "sophisticated balance of experimentation and ideational material," "man-machine interface."
2. Council of Biology Editors' Committee on Graduate Training in Scientific Writing, "Manual on the Teaching of Scientific Writing," in preparation.

APPLICATIONS

1. If you have not already read Woodford's paper, "Sounder Thinking Through Clearer Writing," do it now. The point of view he sets forth can serve you as well in your laboratory or design work as in your writing.

2. Do you agree with the argument that the effort to write clearly leads to clearer thinking? Can you cite specific instances from your own work in which putting your thoughts on paper helped to clarify your problem? Write a brief account of one such instance.

3. For what audience was this paper intended? Does it succeed in reaching these readers? If so, what devices were effective to this end?

4. Study Woodford's Summary, then write a summary of your own for an audience of high school students.

5. In their instructions for contributors the editors of *Science* say, "Use first person, not third; do not use first person plural when singular is appropriate." Mark all instances in which Woodford uses the first person. Does he always use the singular? Do you

see any reason why anyone would consider use of the first person inappropriate?

6. The late Walter S. Campbell used to say that "every composition, every piece of writing which makes sense, embodies the formula:

(1) HEY!   (2) YOU!   (3) SEE?   (4) SO!"[9]

Write a paper explaining how Woodford might have used this formula in developing his argument.

9 Walter S. Campbell, *Writing Non-Fiction* (Boston: The Writer, 1949), p. 49.

2 | Fog and How to Fight It

Did you find the first couple of examples of Dr. Frank Brown's writing about biological clocks (Chapter 1) tough going? If so, there is a perfectly good reason—one that we shall discuss more fully in a moment. For the present, it is enough to point out that all of Brown's work is well written—it is not foggy—-each selection is well suited to its intended audience, even though the styles range from very difficult to quite easy reading.

A seasoned writer like Brown adapts his style to the technical level of his audience by intuition—by the feel of the thing. It is most unlikely, for example, that he consciously told himself at any point, "I shall now adjust my style to the nth-grade level of reading difficulty." But when he wrote the pamphlet *Biological Clocks,* he may very well have kept a roomful of tenth-graders in his mind's eye and written as though he were *talking* to them.

For the less experienced writer an objective test of reading difficulty can be extremely helpful. By an objective test is meant a test that will give the same result no matter who applies it.

The specialist in particular—the scientist, the engineer, the technical student, the technician—almost always writes as though he were addressing an equal or a superior in technical competence. The reason for this is that throughout his school years the specialist has been tuned to writing for such audiences. But when the student approaches the end of his schooling, and especially when he joins professional ranks, he must take a different view of his audience. Then, he will begin to have readers who know a great deal less about his subject than he does. At the same time, he is apt to be quite blind to how hard his writing may be for someone else—he is too familiar with his own subject.

He needs a way to gauge his writing, and the most effective device for this is a simple numerical test that he himself can apply to test his own work.

Enter: The Fog Index

A good many methods for testing level of reading difficulty have been developed over the years. The test recommended here is the Fog Index, developed by Robert Gunning. It is easy to apply, it has been shown in many studies since 1944 to give consistent and reliable indications of readability, and it has proved widely useful in practical applications in industry and government. Moreover, the numerical values of the Fog Index correspond quite closely to levels of reading difficulty by school grade.

Here is how to find the Fog Index of any passage:

One: Jot down the number of words in successive sentences. If the piece is long, you may wish to take several samples of 100 words, spaced evenly through it. If you do, stop the sentence count with the sentence which ends nearest the 100-word total. Divide the total number of words in the passage by the number of sentences. This gives the average sentence length of the passage.

Two: Count the number of words of three syllables or more per

100 words. Don't count the words (1) that are capitalized, (2) that are combinations of short easy words (like "bookkeeper" and "butterfly"), (3) that are verb forms made three syllables by adding -ed or -es (like "created" or "trespasses"). This gives you the percentage of hard words in the passage.

Three: To get the Fog Index, total the two factors just counted and multiply by 0.4.[1]

Two words of caution. A "sentence" in Gunning's terms is not always the distance between a capital letter and a period. Each independent clause[2] is counted as a sentence. What is a "word" sometimes causes problems, too; for our purposes we may define a word as *anything* with white space on either side of it.

Now, let us find the Fog Index of a tongue-in-cheek comment on the kind of engineering writing that appears in some national publications. (Pay no attention to the italics; they will be explained shortly.)

It is the *opinion* of the writer that it is the *appropriate* moment to *re-examine* the style of writing which might most *effectively* be used by members of the *engineering profession*. It is also the writer's belief that a long-lasting *tradition* about the *inappropriateness* of the active voice and the *personal* pronoun for *technical* writing has made for a great deal of *inefficiency*. This kind of writing has been *exemplified* in the past by *numerous national publications*. It would appear that an *application* of the *principles* of *engineering* to the problem would be *beneficial* and it would seem the result might be that such a style would be *eliminated*.[3]

The number of words in each sentence of this passage is: 31–33–14–17–14. (Note that the last "sentence" has two independent clauses and is therefore counted as two sentences.) The total number of words in the passage is 109. This figure divided by

---

[1] From *The Technique of Clear Writing* (New York: McGraw-Hill, 1952), pp. 36–37, and used with written permission of the copyright owner, Robert Gunning, Blacklick, Ohio.

[2] An independent clause, sometimes called a main clause, is a group of words that makes a complete statement—no matter what punctuation comes before or after. Such a clause can stand as a regular sentence, beginning with a capital letter and ending with a period. Or, several independent clauses may be separated by semicolons or by commas. J. N. Hook's parody of Julius Caesar contains three independent clauses: "She came, I saw, she conquered."

[3] Robert L. Shurter, "Let's Take the Strait Jacket off Technical Style," *Mechanical Engineering,* 74 (August, 1952), 664.

5 (the number of sentences) gives the average sentence length— 22 words.

The words of three syllables or more are italicized in the passage. There are 20 of them, or 18 percent.

Adding the average sentence length and the percentage of polysyllabics gives 40. And this multiplied by 0.4 results in a Fog Index of 16. This corresponds to the reading level of a college senior; it is obviously absurd to present an idea this simple at such a high level of reading difficulty.

Of course, the effect was intentional. In his article, Shurter goes on to translate the thought into this:

I think it's about time we stop insisting on impersonal style for engineers. I think that our national publications could set a good example in breaking this strait jacket. After all, the engineer wants efficiency and a "common-sense" approach to his professional work. Why not encourage him to apply this practical method to his writing? If he does, he'll save time, money, material, and his reader's temper.[4]

Stop now, and find the Fog Index of this revised passage. (If you did not get 12.5, try again.) Were any ideas of consequence lost in the revision?

In Chapter 1, we saw a table picturing the widely different audiences that read periodicals of various levels of difficulty. It is important to see more specifically how different periodicals line up in level of reading difficulty. Fog Index comparisons are well suited for this. Table 2.1, based on hundreds of samples taken over a period of many years, shows the level of reading difficulty of various popular magazines by Fog Index and by corresponding school grade.

As a guide for technical writing, however, we need to extend such a table into the more difficult reading ranges of the technical and professional journals. We can get a rough approximation of this by examining the five examples that were given in Chapter 1, under "The General Audience." The Fog Index values for each of these examples are shown in Table 2.2.

It is important to realize that Table 2.2 is not strictly com-

4 *Ibid.*

TABLE 2.1 | **Reading Level**

Fog Index	By Grade	By Magazine	Range
17	College graduate		Area of technical
16	College senior		and professional
15	College junior		journals. No pop-
14	College sophomore		ular magazine
13	College freshman		this difficult.
12	High school senior	*Atlantic Monthly*	"Class"
11	High school junior	*Harper's*	magazines.
10	High school sophomore	*Time*	
9	High school freshman	*Reader's Digest*	
8	Eighth grade	*Ladies' Home Journal*	Easy
7	Seventh grade	*True Confessions*	reading.
6	Sixth grade	Comics	

SOURCE: Robert Gunning, *The Technique of Clear Writing* (New York: McGraw-Hill, 1952), p. 38.

parable to Table 2.1. The data for Table 2.1 were taken by Gunning and his staff from a great many samples. Table 2.2, on the other hand, is based in single samples of one paragraph each and therefore gives only a general indication of the average level of reading difficulty of these periodicals.

TABLE 2.2 | **Reading Level**

Fog Index*	By Grade	By Periodical
28 (28.2)	Genius	*Physiological Zoology*
25 (24.6)	Ph.D.	*Biological Bulletin*
24 (23.7)	M.S.+	*Science*
14 (13.9)	College sophomore	*Scientific American*
13 (13.4)	College freshman	*Saturday Evening Post*

* The numbers to the right of the decimal point are not considered significant; they are given here for the reader's convenience in checking his own count.

Two comments should be made about the numbers in this table. First, the Fog Index of 14 for *Scientific American,* even though it is based in a single sample, happens to fall in the right range; for a random sample of fifteen passages from issues of *Scientific American* from 1958 to 1964, this author found a mean Fog Index of 15.2, plus statistical evidence that the mean of any other fifteen samples would not differ from this value by more than 0.6.

Second, the Fog Index of 13 for *Saturday Evening Post* is high. The example quoted is from one of the "Adventures of the Mind" series, and these had a higher level of reading difficulty than most *Post* copy.

Now, how does all this apply to the practical problems of writing a good technical report?

As we shall see in the next chapter, the Westinghouse Electric Corporation has made an extensive study of just what kinds of writing management men want in the technical report. What is the top level of reading difficulty they will accept? Here is their statement:

If the report is to convey information effectively, all parts of it *should preferably* be written at the level of articles published in *The Scientific American*. And, all parts of the report other than the body and the appendix, *must* be written at *The Scientific American* level. The highly technical, mathematical, and other detailed material—if necessary at all—can and should be placed in the appendix.[5]

Specification of the *Scientific American* level does establish a norm and does provide the report writer with a model to emulate. But the writer still faces two problems: First, will this level be acceptable to his own readers (that is, are the preferences of Westinghouse management representative of what report readers in general want)? Second, is a readability test as useful for technical reports as for other kinds of writing?

Until very recently, there were no satisfactory answers to these questions. Independent ratings by seasoned technical men of the effectiveness of written materials have not been available to compare with readability scores; and very little readability testing has been done at the more difficult levels of workaday technical writing. To find answers, the present author carried out a nation-

[5] James W. Souther, "What Management Wants in the Technical Report," *Journal of Engineering Education,* 52 (April, 1962), 498–503.

wide survey of the opinions of scientists, engineers, and technical management men in twenty prominent research, development, and manufacturing organizations throughout the country.[6]

In this survey, a panel of ninety-six technical men judged in two ways the effectiveness of twenty examples selected from the literature of science and engineering. These men had an average experience of nearly twenty-five years after the bachelor's degree, and more than half of them hold the doctorate. The selections to be judged ranged in reading difficulty from eighth-grade level to postdoctorate specialist level.

The panel members ranked the examples in order from 1 to 20 according to their own judgments of the effectiveness of the writing for arriving at critical conclusions or making important decisions. These rankings were then correlated with those from seven published readability formulas.[7] Good agreement was found between the judges' evaluations and the test scores.[8] Since the Fog Index is simple and easy to apply, it was considered suitable for routine use by technical writers.

The judges also rated the twenty examples on a scale of very poor–poor–fair–good–very good. Those in the "good" range had Fog Index levels close to 15. This, you will recall, is the average level of *Scientific American* and supports the Westinghouse recommendation. Further, the examples that had Fog Index levels much above 15 were rated by the panel as "fair" to "very poor," and those below 15 were rated "good" to "very good."

In short, an experienced report writer can feel that he is on safe ground if he maintains an average Fog Index no higher than 15.

What then of the scientist or engineer who is approaching the task earlier in his career? For him the following comments are offered:

[6] Ritchie R. Ward, "Readability of Technical Writing," *Proceedings, 14th International Communications Conference,* Society of Technical Writers and Publishers, Chicago (May, 1967), p. 32.

[7] Fog Index; Farr-Jenkins-Paterson; Flesch formality/popularity; Dale-Chall; Gillie; Danielson-Bryan; Flesch reading ease. For discussion and references to the original literature, see George R. Klare, *The Measurement of Readability* (Ames: Iowa State University Press, 1963).

[8] Except the Flesch formality/popularity formula, which was designed primarily for other kinds of writing.

- Write your first drafts *as rapidly as you can.*
- *After* you have written, check the Fog Index values of random samples.
- Do not be surprised if you find passages that test as high as 30!
- Rework your first drafts to bring the average Fog Index down to *12 or lower.*
- Soon, your writing will become clearer, brisker, more muscular—with the added bonus that it will also be easier to do.

Plain and Fancy

There are many ways to reduce the Fog Index of any piece of writing. From the nature of the formula you can see that the obvious ways are to trim sentence lengths and to trade long words for short.

Use plain words and phrases instead of fancy ones. The fancy type are those that we tend to use almost without thinking; they come so naturally in our everyday speech that they creep into our writing in a very sneaky way. Search them out in all your work, and prune them drastically.

Here is a list of common offenders, together with suggested plainer forms. Obviously such a list should be used with judgment; use the suggested word or phrase only if it truly expresses your intended meaning. When an employee is fired, the personnel director says that he was "terminated." In such official jargon, no other word will do. On the other hand, a laboratory experiment is better "ended" or "stopped" than "terminated."

INSTEAD OF	TRY	INSTEAD OF	TRY
accomplish	do	as though	if
achieve	do	as to	about, on
acquire	get	as to why	why
add an additional	add	at all times	always
additionally	also	at the present time	now
anticipate	expect	at the time of	during
any and all	any, all	at the time that	while
appear	seem	at this time	now
appreciate	be grateful for	be acquainted with	know
arise	get up	be associated with	work for (or with)
ascertain	find out		
assist	help	be aware of	know

INSTEAD OF	TRY	INSTEAD OF	TRY
by means of	with, in, by	in the event that	if
calculated to	likely to	in the immediate	
commence	begin, start	vicinity of	near
consensus of opinion	consensus	in the majority of	most
consider	think of	in the near future	soon
consult	ask	in the neighborhood of	about
contemplate	think of	in view of the fact that	because, since
continue on	continue	locality	place
contribute	give	locate	find
deem	think	make the acquaint-	
desire	want to, wish	ance of	meet
despite the fact that	although	materially	much
determine	find out	necessitate	call for
divulge	say, tell	new innovation	innovation
donate	give	obtain	get
during the course of	during	on account of the fact	
each and every one	each	that	because
employ	use	on behalf of	for
endeavor	try	on the order of	about
equally as	equally	optimistic	hopeful
evidence	show	peruse	read
experience	feel	place	put
facilitate	make easy	position	job
for the purpose of	for, to	possibly may	may
for the reason that	because	presently	now
forward	send	presume	suppose
general consensus	consensus	previous to	before
had reference to	meant	primary	first
if and when	if, when	prior to	before
in a manner similar to	to, like	purchase	buy
in a position to	can	qualified expert	expert
in all probability	probabiy	realize	know
inasmuch as	because, since	recall	remember
in connection with	in	receive	get
indicate	show	refer back	refer
individual	person	regret	be sorry
in excess of	more than	relative to	of
inform	tell	remark	say
initiate	begin, start	render	make
in order to	to	reply	answer
inquire	ask	require	call for, need
in regard to	about, on	reside	live
in relation to	for	response	answer
in respect of	of	retain	keep

INSTEAD OF	TRY	INSTEAD OF	TRY
reveal	show	thus	so
rise	get up	to all intents and	
seek	look for	purposes	so
so as to	so	transmit	send
state	say	transpire	happen
subsequent to	after	until such time as	until
subsequently	later	utilize	use
substantially	much	with respect to	about, in, to
sufficient	enough	with the exception of	except (for)
take place	happen	would seem	seem
terminate	end, stop		

$P + T + P' = R$

Before you have used this list for very long, you will realize how much plain forms can improve the clarity of your writing. What you have done is to reduce *wordiness*—perhaps the worst of all enemies of sentence clarity.

But no such list can be complete, and you need guiding principles to carry you beyond dependence on lists. These principles may be best expressed in rhetorical language. Like the scientist or engineer, the rhetorician uses many technical terms to express in brief the specialized ideas he deals with. A combination of such jargon terms is symbolized in the mock equation above. In it:

P = *pleonasm* = using more words than are needed to express an idea; *overloading*.

T = *tautology* = repeating an idea in different words without adding force or clarity; *deadwood*.

P' = *periphrasis* = talking around a subject rather than to the heart of it; *circumlocution*.

R = *redundancy* = using P, T, and P' either separately or in combination; *wordiness*.

Here are examples of *P, T,* and *P'*, together with suggested improvements.

Pleonasm: "A flabby, verbose sentence, if not downright unclear, often has a narcotic effect on the reader so that he fails to see the clarity that is there."

Improved: "A flabby, verbose sentence, if not downright unclear, will drug its reader into inattention.[9]

Tautology: " 'A beginner who has just started' is a tautology."[10]

Improved: A bare beginner is not one.

Periphrasis: " 'The answer is in the negative' is a periphrasis for 'no.' "[11]

The burden of this chapter will now be clear; to write effectively, you should write as simply and directly as you can.

"But," you may object, "this will not lead to mature writing. With all this simplification, I haven't any tools left to write with. How can I develop a good style?"

The question is close to the point, of course. Nevertheless, if you are a less experienced writer or if you have done some writing but are still having problems, you may well recall Alexander Pope's couplet:

> Not to go back is somewhat to advance,
> And men must walk, at least, before they dance.

The dancing lessons will come later in this book. The devices for attaining a mature prose style make for absorbing study, and we deal with them at some length. After such study and some practice, you may then be able to turn out prose like the following, written by two chemists for the introduction to their advanced textbook:

There are ancient cathedrals which, apart from their consecrated purpose, inspire solemnity and awe. Even the curious visitor speaks of serious things, with hushed voice, and as each whisper reverberates through the vaulted nave, the returning echo seems to bear a message of mystery. The labor of generations of architects and artisans has long been forgotten, the scaffolding erected for their toil has long since been removed, their mistakes have been erased, or have become hidden by the dust of centuries. Seeing only the perfection of the completed whole, we are impressed as by some superhuman agency. But sometimes we enter such an edifice that is still partly under construction; then the sound of hammers, the reek of tobacco, the trivial jests bandied from

9 Hulon Willis, *Structure, Style, Usage: A Guide to Expository Writing* (New York: Holt, Rinehart and Winston, 1964), p. 112.

10 *Webster's Third New International Dictionary, Unabridged* (Springfield: Merriam, 1964), p. 2344.

11 *Time,* quoted in *ibid.,* p. 1681.

workman to workman, enable us to realize that these great structures are but the result of giving to ordinary human effort a direction and a purpose.[12]

Turn now to "Scientific Writing and the General Problem of Communication," by D. O. Hebb and Dalbir Bindra of McGill University. This paper was written before several of the current readability formulas were available and limits its discussion to the Flesch reading ease scale, cited earlier. Most of the formulas, however, are similar to this in principle, and much of what Hebb and Bindra say about the Flesch scale would apply to any of them.

A good deal of irresponsible nonsense has been written in criticism of readability formulas, but Hebb and Bindra take a fair-minded look at their advantages and limitations.

[12] G. N. Lewis and Merle Randall, *Thermodynamics and the Free Energy of Chemical Substances* (New York: McGraw-Hill, 1923; rev. 1961), p. v.

Scientific Writing
and the General Problem
of Communication

D. O. Hebb and Dalbir Bindra

*Donald O. Hebb and Dalbir Bindra are professors of psychology
at McGill University, Montreal. Professor Hebb was chairman
of the Department of Psychology at McGill from 1948 to 1958;
his chief interests have been comparative and physiological psychology. Professor Bindra is past president of the Canadian
Psychological Association and has contributed in the fields of
emotion, motivation, and experimental psychopathology.*

WE HAVE RECENTLY HAD OCCASION TO CONSIDER WHAT SORT
of guidance can be given to graduate students in their scientific writing, especially in the use of Flesch's methods (2, 3)
for appraising the effectiveness of written English. There has
been some recent discussion of the problem, but it seems to
us that some of its larger aspects have not been formulated
clearly.

We approach the problem with Boring's assumption (1)
that doing an experiment is not more important than writing

The American Psychologist, 7 (October, 1952), 569–573. Used by permission of the American Psychological Association and the authors.

it up for publication. A solitary student might conceivably experiment and theorize to satisfy his own curiosity, but a study that is unreported does not contribute to public knowledge. It does not advance science. Even more: a study that is reported but does not get read is no better than one that remains unpublished. It is therefore the scientist's business to write in a way that increases the likelihood that his paper will be read as well as understood. We shall simply take it for granted in this discussion that precision is of first importance in scientific writing; having assumed that, we are concerned here with the question of *readability,* the property of writing that attracts a reader and holds his attention. As far as he can achieve it, readability is as important for the scientific writer as it is for the novelist.

How is readability to be improved? Clearly it would help to have some objective index to show where one has strayed from the path of virtue, a literary Wasserman test to show what writing is in good health and what needs treatment. But readability must be a complex quality and any single score would be a very rough index indeed. We believe that the Flesch count (2) did have merit as a rough index of some of the factors in readability, but it is not surprising that Flesch has felt it necessary to abandon this single index in favor of two independent ones (3).

The earlier Flesch count was arrived at by counting affixes in words and words in sentences, combined with a count of the number of references to persons. It gave some useful information about scientific writing, and was at once recognized as valuable by instructors in psychology, if only for applying to their graduate students and not to themselves. That it had shortcomings was also seen promptly, and Flesch's later scheme (3) has tried to get around the defects.

Two scores are now provided: one representing *reading ease* (a difficulty index, based on word and sentence lengths), the other *human interest* (number of references to persons). The scores are arranged to run from 0 to 100. A top score of 100 on reading ease means that the material will be understood by people who have got through grade four; top score on human interest indicates "enough human interest to suit the reading skills and habits of a barely 'functionally literate' person" (3, p. 225). As one might expect, scientific writing scores low on both scales, fiction and comics score high, with good nonfiction in between.

This change certainly improves things. The earlier Flesch count simply said that *Reader's Digest* is more readable than the *New Yorker,* a decision that some of us might question. The new scales say that *Reader's Digest* has greater reading ease, the *New Yorker* greater human interest, a more acceptable conclusion. The earlier count made Koffka (5) more readable than James (4), which was a state of affairs that made Harvard men shudder (7). It is now suggested that such a reversal of form occurred only because the earlier single scale did not give James enough credit for the human interest of his writings.

This putting-Koffka-in-his-place seems to have so pleased some psychologists that they have come to consider the new Flesch scales as giving a valid account of scientific writing, a good estimate of its effectiveness as communication. Reprints of Flesch's article are available in many departments (including our own) and graduate students are encouraged to use it. This being so, and considering the importance of good writing in science, let us see what the value of Flesch's method is and what it is not.

Flesch's Two Scales

We propose first that the human-interest scale be forgotten completely, at least for the appraisal of scientific writing. Even if it is true that mentioning people enlarges the audience of interested readers (by including the less literate), it does not follow that within a literate scientific group the same relation holds. The same piece of writing may appeal very differently to different groups. The changes one would make in the *Yale Review* in order to increase its subway sale might lead to its disappearance from the shelves of the University Book Club. Scientists by common consent are peculiar people with peculiar reading habits, and any scale of human interest for general use has doubtful validity for scientific journals. Scientists are also human, and do often read *Reader's Digest* . . . , but not at moments when they are thinking about an experimental problem. Mixing up one interest with another may spoil the pleasure of both.

At any rate, it is not yet clear that references to human beings in a scientific paper have any value for increasing its readability. Perhaps this may be shown in the future. At present, we believe, the human-interest scale simply distracts attention from the real problem of how to use the second scale, the measure of reading ease.

The proper use of this second scale requires that we recognize two things. One is that reading difficulty is not only the difficulty of understanding words and sentences; there is also the way the sentences are related to one another in the paragraph, and paragraphs in the chapter or section. A measure of word or sentence difficulty will undoubtedly correlate with over-all difficulty, but it should cause no surprise to find that there are writers whose words are simple and whose sentences are short, but whose writings are impossible to read. With such a writer, the Flesch scale of reading ease will be totally misleading. There is no scale at present for measuring this larger aspect of readability, but because one has no measure for it one must not forget it. To this problem we shall return in the following section.

The second point one should consider about the scale of reading ease is that comprehensibility is not simply and directly related to readability (the property of reading matter that keeps a reader's nose in the book). In other words, making something easier does not always make it more interesting or desirable. It is true that using simpler words and shorter sentences makes writing comprehensible to a larger fraction of the general population, but this relation cannot be construed to mean that for any given segment of the population (artists, plumbers, scientists) an increase in comprehensibility will necessarily make for an increase in readability.

Rather, we feel, for any homogeneous group of a particular educational level the relation between reading ease and readability is likely to be described by one of the curves in Figure 1: a certain optimum level of difficulty may be required to make the material maximally readable; too easy or too difficult writing will decrease

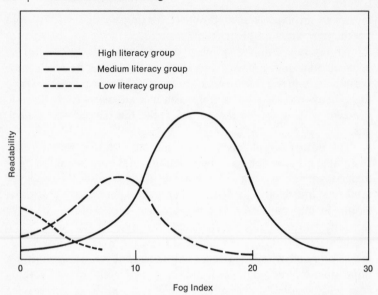

Figure 1. Relation between subjective readability and readability formula scores, as suggested by Hebb and Bindra. [Since the reader is already familiar with Fog Index numbers, these rather than Flesch reading-ease scores are shown on the abscissa.—Ed.]

readability. Thus it will usually happen that an increase of reading ease, in most scientific manuscripts, would increase readability, because as scientists we generally write too long sentences and make too much use of big words. But the thing can be overdone, and a reading-ease score of 100 would certainly not be a recommendation for a scientific paper. The reader may feel that this danger is remote, but there is at least one recent textbook that we find unreadable because it appears to be aimed at the lowest quartile of the freshman class. An occasional use of the Flesch scale to bring word and sentence difficulty *up* to an adult standard would also be justified.

Thus there are two reasons for denying that the Flesch scale of reading ease is a measure of readability. One is that man enjoys a certain amount of difficulty in his undertakings and is bored by what is too easy. The easiest writing is not the most readable. The second reason, that the scale really measures only one of the factors in reading ease, offers a greater problem: we cannot suggest any measure of the remaining factors that are inherent in the larger organization of a piece of writing, and yet they must be taken into account in one's own writing and when one is trying to show a student how to write better. Let us look at this problem next.

The Essential Problem of Verbal Communication

The difficulty we are concerned with here is best seen by first considering the psychological problem of comprehending spoken rather than written language. The task that a speaker sets his listener is to achieve a two- or three-dimensional structure from a series in one dimension. It is the task of making a house *at once* out of a series of nails, boards, scantlings, and bricks delivered one at a time in a rapid series. (Conversely, at the speaker's end, it is the task of taking the house to pieces just as rapidly, and shipping the parts in the right order to allow the receiver to put it together right.) It is precisely the problem of television, to create a picture in two dimensions out of a series of events that have no locus and vary only in the degree of energy delivered from moment to moment; or the problem of the army commander whose men arrive on the field of action single file, though he must use them together distributed over the field in an organized two-dimensional pattern. Essentially, it is the problem of transforming a temporal pattern into a spatial one.

That is, though the sounds of speech are received seriatim, their effects on behavior are not seriatim and discrete. The response to one of the stimuli (words) arriving at any moment may be quite indeterminate, and become determinate only after the arrival of another stimulus as much as 5, 10, or 15 seconds later. Thus earlier stimuli must often be "held" until the later ones are delivered, these determining the significance of (the response to be evoked by) the earlier ones. This integration of discrete serial stimuli is shown on one's ability to disentangle a spoonerism (6); but also in understanding such ordinary sentences as "Whether it is large or small, you should always keep your dog on a leash" (here the first phrase with *it* can hardly have the same determinate effect as "whether *your dog* is large or small"); or even "There is hardly any bread in the house" (where the idea of "there is hardly any" must be, to say the least, a highly indeterminate one, until the noun arrives to allow the listener to give the first four words their significance).

In reading, the problem is not quite the same as in listening: the reader who has failed to "hold" the first words of the sentence can readily go back after reading the later ones (in effect reordering the sentence). In reading, also, we may take in a word or a short phrase as a whole, not receiving the letters separately as the ear must do with its sounds. But the phrases and sentences must come seriatim, and so must paragraphs and sections. An introductory sentence in a paragraph may be fully understood only after the last sentence has been read; or the last sentence may be comprehensible only with the set, or expectancy, established by the first. As to the larger organization of written work, it is a common experience to find that one can read a scientific paper better by first reading its summary. Writers find it advisable sometimes to begin a paper by adumbrating their conclusions, for the same reason. Thus with written matter the problem is modified by the reader's ability to skip about and reread when he wants to, but in principle the fundamental difficulty of verbal communication remains: to get an over-view of a complicated structure that must be apprehended bit by bit.

For the length of a short paragraph, the required integration presents no great difficulty to the skilled reader. At this level, punctuation is also a very effective tool. It keeps the reader informed as to what goes with what; and paragraphing itself is a similar aid. At higher levels of organization, however, there are few comparable aids, and here it is that the skilled reader's problem really begins. Here too Flesch's method is of no use in estimating the extent to which a writer has helped his readers.

When it comes to "holding" a long series of paragraphs while sorting out the next one, and piling set upon set, the reader's difficulties become acute; and it is here as much as anywhere that the intelligibility of scientific writing is determined. It does not lie simply in the use of short words or short sentences (still less in multifarious social reference). To a major extent it lies in the way in which the writer helps the reader reassemble his battalions, shipped to him man by man. Figuratively, "Here begins your second battalion," "the next fifty are headquarters staff," "place the following thousand in reserve"—which in practice might take the form, "So much for the first point," "Let me remind the reader that we are now discussing only A, not B or C," or "An alternative to the foregoing is . . ."

A most important difference between the writings of James and Koffka, referred to earlier, is the amount of help given the reader in making a coherent picture out of paragraph after paragraph, and section after section, of difficult argument. James organizes his battalions well, he keeps the reader aware of the main line of thought even while digressing from it, he maintains the outline of the picture he is trying to paint while he is filling in the detail; but with Koffka one is lost in detail as he goes from one experiment to the next, the main picture does not become steadily clearer as the details of experimentation are supplied. James's writing makes a good gestalt, Koffka's does not.

What Advice to the Neophyte?

It is dangerous to write about good writing. The reader is more than likely to say "Ah, so they think they can tell us how to write—let's see how well *they* do!" Our purpose here is not to offer a sample of perfect work but to consider the difficulties we all face in writing. It does seem, however, that there is a little advice to be offered, and in order to be on the safe side we offer it only to the neophyte.

Perhaps the first piece of advice is to keep on being a neophyte throughout one's professional life. Writing is an art, ultimately, and there is no set of rules that will guarantee success, nor can the writer hope to reach perfection. One must know the rules of usage, grammar, sentence structure; but one never knows for sure how all the rules are to be applied in a particular case. The final product must be a matter of individual judgment, just as the painter who knows the rules of color mixture, perspective, and so on must still add something of his own that makes him an artist.

One of the things for which there are few rules is the larger organization discussed in the preceding section. The traditional heads of the scientific paper, Introduction, Method, Results, Conclusions, Summary, are generally useful. But this particular convention sometimes must be modified; and its use is not enough by itself to guarantee clarity. Subheads within the section are often a further help; yet another rule probably should always be followed, to depend as little as possible on heads and subheads and try to write so as to be clear if all headings were removed. This means that the signposts of organization should be incorporated in the text, and made as unobtrusive as they can be.

There is no index of success at this level except the reader himself: does he have to labor to read, or not? We need not repeat the old advice to write and lay the writing away until one can more nearly see it from the reader's point of view; or better, to have a colleague read the manuscript *and then take his criticism seriously.* What we might add to the advice is this: The writer will often not agree with the critic's specific proposals; but apart from questions of style, he should *always* assume that some change is needed in the passage to which the critic objects, even if it is not the change that has been recommended. It is worth adding further that all this applies still to us neophytes who have been writing for 10 or 20 years. The writer is unfortunate who does not have colleagues who will take the trouble to read and advise on his manuscripts; and the time one spends on a colleague's manuscript is not wasted, for a serious attempt to help someone else is one of the best ways to learn more about one's own writing.

Finally, on the artistic side, we should like to urge that the writer cultivate his ear for the rhythms of English prose. This sounds formidable but is not. We are talking only about the ordinary, everyday readability of sentence and paragraph, not implying that one should aim at writing great literature for the psychological journals. All of us have an ear that comes from reading as well as listening to spoken English, but not all of us make the most of it in our writing. The practical advice of this paper is simply to try *listening* to the phrases and sentences as one silently reads the manuscript, and to modify them freely not only for sense but (in a modest way) for euphony too. If one attends to it, one will often find that this sentence is too long—not in itself, but because the preceding ones were long also; or that another somehow needs another phrase *here* for balance, or should be a little longer to sound right. Everyone does this now, but perhaps unwittingly; what we suggest is that a conscious effort at euphony, to make one's sentences *sound right* as well as making them clear, can pay dividends in readability and therefore in the effectiveness of scientific communication.

So our advice to the neophyte is this. Take the problem of writing seriously; assume that it is as difficult and as important as the investigation to be reported; write and rewrite,* aiming for both clarity and ease; and get and use all the criticism you can from others. You must know the rules of usage and grammar, and Fowler's *Modern English Usage* should be your Bible, to be used with all the reverence and skepticism that is due to a Bible. It will be salutary to use Flesch's scale of reading ease once or twice on your own writing, but you might also read and reread Quiller-Couch's *On the Art of Writing*. Develop your ear for phrase and sentence, on the one hand, and on the other keep working at the art that none of us will ever fully master, of using complicated detail to build a simple outline of main ideas for the reader. As Boring (1) puts it, good writing is good manners: your problem is both to please and to help your public. This you can do only when you learn how to be the first victim of your writing, how to anticipate a reader's difficulties and to hear yourself as others hear you.

References

1. Boring, E. G., "Another note on scientific writing," *Science* 84 (1936), 457–459.
2. Flesch, R., *The Art of Plain Talk* (New York: Harper, 1946).
3. Flesch, R., "A new readability yardstick," *J. Appl. Psychol.* 32 (1948), 221–233.
4. James, W., *Principles of Psychology* (New York: Holt, 1890).
5. Koffka, K., *Principles of Gestalt Psychology* (New York: Harcourt, Brace, 1935).

---

* It is a poor paper that would not be better for one more revision.

6. Lashley, K. S., "The problem of serial order in behavior," in L. A. Jeffres (ed.), *Cerebral Mechanisms in Behavior: the Hixon Symposium* (New York: Wiley, 1951).
7. Stevens, S. S., and Stone, G., "Psychological writing, easy and hard," *Amer. Psychologist* 2 (1947), 230–235.

APPLICATIONS

1. "Scientific Writing and the General Problem of Communication" is a personal essay—that is, it is based on the personal observations, opinions, and conclusions of its authors; editors of general magazines would call it a "think piece." In contrast, the paper "Readability of Technical Writing," cited in footnote 6 in this chapter, is a report of an objective study. Turn to the Appendix and read the abstract of the latter paper. Compare and contrast your impressions of the two, and then write a 500-word summary of your own conclusions on the practical usefulness of readability testing in technical writing.

2. Refer to the five examples in Chapter 1, pages 5–7, and find the Fog Index values of each. (Skip the references in parentheses.) Your results should agree with the numbers in Table 2.2.

3. The foregoing examples were taken from the opening paragraphs of each paper. Would you expect that opening paragraphs would usually be representative of the reading level of papers as a whole? Why? Or why not?

4. Find the Fog Index values of typical samples of your own work. If they are high, use some of the devices set forth in this chapter to bring your Index down to 12.

5. Find the Fog Index of the Lewis and Randall passage quoted at the end of this chapter. *Remember that independent clauses are counted as separate sentences.* What does the readability level you find suggest about the qualities of mature prose?

6. Hebb and Bindra feel that Fowler's *Modern English Usage* (New York and Oxford: Oxford University Press, 1926) "should be your Bible." You will note from the publication date that Fowler is now forty years old. It is also very, very British. If you are not already familiar with Fowler, go to your library and leaf

through a copy. Then compare it with one or more of the following recent guides to American usage:

- Bergen Evans and Cornelia Evans, *A Dictionary of Contemporary American Usage* (New York: Random House, 1957).
- Theodore M. Bernstein, *The Careful Writer* (New York: Atheneum, 1965).
- Wilson Follett, *Modern American Usage, A Guide* (New York: Hill & Wang, 1966).

Choose one of these, buy a copy, and keep it beside your dictionary.

7. Compare Sir Arthur Quiller-Couch's *On the Art of Writing* (New York: Putnam, 1916) with William Strunk, Jr., and E. B. White, *The Elements of Style* (New York: Macmillan, 1959). You can buy a copy of Strunk and White in paperback for about a dollar.

PART 2

Your Purpose

3 | What to Report[1]

Picture a supervisor coming in one morning and saying, "Joe, give me a design for an electric motor." Nothing more. And the engineer is at sea; questions tumble through his mind. What voltage? What wattage? A.C. or D.C.? What r.p.m.? And so on and so on . . . He is stopped before he starts.

So it is with the technical report. If the writer lacks a design specification to begin with, he is in for a bad time.

"But," you may object, "that is a ridiculously exaggerated situation."

---

[1] A study of what Westinghouse management men most want to see in their technical reports has been previously published under this same title. The entire text of this study is reprinted with permission later in this chapter. Copyright © 1962, Westinghouse Electric Corporation.

Is it? Let us see.

It took a long time for Reginald O. Kapp, dean of the Faculty of Engineering of the University of London, to find a suitable lecturer for a postgraduate course, the "Presentation of Technical Information," at University College, London.[2] He eventually found his man in B. C. Brookes, who has since been senior lecturer at University College and a consultant on technical writing to British industry.

After extensive first-hand observation, Brookes had this to say about the report-writing problems of industrial scientists:

Now I must consider the scientist in industry, who is not doing research but who is applying his scientific or engineering knowledge to practical ends. Occasionally I am asked to advise industrial organisations about the reports their applied scientists are writing. The samples sent me for inspection usually demonstrate clearly that something is wrong. Grammatical and syntactical faults abound. A superficial examination would lead the critic to conclude that a short revision course in English grammar and some remarks on style appropriate to their apparent needs would meet the situation. It does not. . . .

It is my experience that much of the bad writing complained of in industry arises simply because the authors are uncertain of the purposes of their assignment. A scientist who is uncertain of his purpose or of his subject will reflect his uncertainty in grammatical and syntactical faults, will betray his aimlessness in sudden switches of points of view, and his hesitancy and indecision in the unbalanced and illogical structure of his paper. But a scientist who has something to say and a clear purpose in saying it is usually able to write his paper in a clear plain style that is, with one serious reservation,[3] adequate for the occasion.[4]

Very fortunately, recent studies in this country have thrown a clear, fresh light on what management men want in the technical report. The Westinghouse study mentioned in Chapter 2 is especially helpful, and the best introduction to it is the Westinghouse

2 Reginald O. Kapp, *The Presentation of Technical Information* (New York: Macmillan, 1960), p. IX.

3 Brookes refers to the use of woolly phrases and tired words, which we have already dealt with in part in Chapter 2.

4 B. C. Brookes, "The Teaching of English to Scientists and Engineers," in Randolph Quirk and A. H. Smith, eds., *The Teaching of English* (London: Secker & Warburg, 1959), pp. 144–146.

13. What do you think your boss wants in the reports you send him?
14. What percentage of the reports you receive do you think desirable or useful? (In kind or frequency.)
15. What percentage of the reports you write do you think desirable or useful? (In kind or frequency.)
16. What particular weaknesses have you found in reports?

Each interview took from one-and-one-half to two hours to complete. Professor Souther made minimal notes during the interview and then recorded and expanded these at the end of the day while the answers were still fresh in his mind. The typed interviews were classified and grouped according to supervisory class and level. After that, the material was studied and evaluated. A summary report was sent to each person interviewed with the request that he indicate the need for and the method of adapting the summary report material into report writing guides.

The information feedback defined clearly the dual role in the reporting process: 1) that of the supervisor of the engineer who is writing the report; and 2) that of the engineer who writes the report. As a result, two report writing guides were developed: 1) *Managing Report Writing*—a guide that defines management's supervisory responsibility and that includes a procedure for supervising report writing assignments; and 2) *What to Report*—a guide that defines the author's responsibilities to the management readers of his report and identifies the informational needs of management.

Mark Twain said that everybody talks about the weather but nobody does anything about it. Literally hundreds of management men in industry and government have complained about the poor writing turned out by their scientists and engineers. Now Westinghouse has done something about it. Turn to *What to Report,* and read it with care. You will note that it contains invaluable check lists against which you can check the subject content of every report you write. Obviously the Westinghouse Corporation's chief emphasis is on the technical manufacturing process, but you should have little difficulty in transferring the underlying principles all the way from a fundamental research paper to a sales development brochure.

What to Report

REPORT *reading* CAN BE ALMOST AS TIME CONSUMING FOR management as report *writing* can be for the engineer. Not infrequently, a report is badly organized and written simply because the writer does not have an accurate picture of who will be reading his report and what they want to know.

Without a thorough knowledge of his reader's needs, no writer can do a really effective job. In the end, both the writing and the reading tasks can be greatly simplified by a better understanding of the particular informational needs of management.

Westinghouse Electric Corporation (Pittsburgh © 1962). Used by permission.

What Management Looks for in Technical Reports

The information needs of management vary according to job responsibility, supervisory experience, and educational background.

Therefore, the informational content of the report is determined by the prospective readers of the report, and this is something that the manager must determine for individual cases.

However, despite these variations, there is remarkable agreement among all managers on what they look for in technical reports. Our study discloses these common requirements:

- They look for pertinent facts and competent opinions that will aid them in decision making.
- They want to know quickly whether to read the report, route it, or skip it.
- To determine this, they want answers to some or all of the following questions:

  > What's the report about and who wrote it?
  > What does it contribute?
  > What are the conclusions and recommendations?
  > What are their importance and significance?
  > What's the implication to the Company?
  > What actions are suggested? Long range? Short range?
  > Why? By whom? When? How?

- They want the information in brief, concise and meaningful terms, at the beginning of the report, and all in one piece.

Approach to Writing

The point of attack in report writing is the analysis of the problem. An effective report, like any good engineered product, must be designed to fill a particular purpose in a specific situation. Effective design depends on a detailed analysis of the problem and an awareness of the factors involved. In analyzing your writing problem, you should ask the following questions:

- What is the purpose of the report?
- Who will read it?
- How will it be used?
- Why is the report wanted?

- What is wanted?
- When is it wanted?
- What decisions will be based on the report?
- What does the reader need to be told in order to understand the material?

Once this analysis has been completed and the influencing factors defined, you should evaluate your material and select that to be included in the report, using the analysis as a basis for your selection. The material should then be organized functionally within the requirements of the reporting situation just as an engineering design must be functional within its technical and environmental requirements. If the analysis of the problem was thorough, you are reader-oriented, and writing the report becomes a much easier task.

In organizing and writing your report, you must make certain to:

- Include only essential material.
- Arrange it for ease of use.
- Set the material in perspective.
- Relate it to other work.
- Interpret its meaning and significance.
- Support it with effective illustrations and good layout.
- Write it for the reader.

Determining Content

When writing for management, you should place emphasis on the most important concepts: the conclusions, the recommendations, the implications, and the significant contributions of the work you are reporting. The management reader immediately wants to know:

1. What is the report about?
2. What does it contribute?
3. What action should be taken?

Sound management decisions must be based on pertinent facts and qualified opinions. To aid in decision making, management wants to know what you, the specialist close to the problem, think about it. What are the pertinent facts as you see them? In your considered judgment, how should they be interpreted? What conclusions do you draw and what recommendations do you make? Where you can see implications to other departments, divisions, and the Company, you should include this information to guide management.

In making decisions, management must consider a variety of factors and draw on the work and qualified opinions of the Westinghouse organization.

Engineering is the primary source of information on technical problems, new projects and products, tests and experiments, materials and processes, and field troubles and special design problems. The following questions represent the informational needs of management in each of these areas. You should supply whatever information and assistance you can.

PROBLEMS

What is it?

Why undertaken?

Magnitude and importance?

What is being done? By whom?

Approaches used?

Thorough and complete?

Suggested solution? Best? Consider others?

What now? Who does it?

Time factors?

NEW PROJECTS AND PRODUCTS

Potential?

Risks?

Scope of application?

Commercial implications?

Competition?

Importance to Company?

More work to be done? Any problems?

Required manpower, facilities and equipment?

Relative importance to other projects or products?

Life of project or product line?
Effect on Westinghouse technical position?
Priorities required?
Proposed schedule?
Target date?

TESTS AND EXPERIMENTS

What tested or investigated?
Why?
How?
What did it show?
Better ways?
Conclusions?
Recommendations?
Implications to Company?

MATERIALS AND PROCESSES

Properties, characteristics, capabilities?
Limitations?
Use requirements and environment?
Areas and scope of application?
Cost factors?
Availability and sources?
What else will do it?
Problems in using?
Significance of application to Company?

FIELD TROUBLES AND SPECIAL DESIGN PROBLEMS

Specific equipment involved?
What trouble developed?
How much involved?
Any trouble history?
Responsibility? Others? Westinghouse?
Special requirements and environment?
What is needed?

Who does it?
Time factors?
Most practical solution?
Recommended action?
Suggested product design changes?

In addition, management must also consider market and organizational factors. Although these factors are not primarily the concern of engineering, you should be aware of them and should provide information whenever technical aspects provide special evidence or insight into the problems being considered.

MARKET FACTORS

Chances for success?
Possible rewards?
Risks?
Can we be competitive?
Is there a market? Must one be created?
Competitive position?
When available?

ORGANIZATIONAL FACTORS

Is it the type of work Westinghouse should do?
Require changes? Organizational? Manpower? Facility and equipment?
Expanding or contracting program?
What suffers if we concentrate on this?

Arranging Material

Once the content of the report has been determined, the next step is to organize the material and structure the report so that it will be useful to its readers. The precise information managers want in a report is, of course, determined by their management responsibilities, but how they want it presented is determined by their reading habits. Here also the study revealed some useful information.

For our purposes, a technical report is assumed to have seven parts: (1) Title and Author; (2) a Summary (or Abstract); (3) Introduction; (4) Background Information; (5) Body (or Discussion); (6) Conclusions and Recommendations; and (7) Appendix.

Here's what the study showed:

- Every manager interviewed said he reads the *Summary* or Abstract.
- A bare majority said they read the *Introduction, Background, Conclusions and Recommendations.*
- Few managers said they read the *Body*, or Discussion, or the *Appendix*.

Moreover, the survey showed the *sequence* of reading was usually the same as the above listing. This does not necessarily suggest that the organization of reports should be in the above order, but it is a strong recommendation that the summary should be placed immediately after the title and author.

If the summary is to convey information effectively, it should contain three kinds of facts:

1. *What the report is about.* This includes a definition of the problem; a statement of the objectives; a reason for doing the work expressed in terms of new products or increased profits for Westinghouse; a statement of the conclusions reached; and a statement of the recommendations made.
2. *The significance and implications of the work.* This should include a definitive statement about the importance of the investigation, followed by an interpretive statement of results suggested by the facts.
3. *The actions called for.* This includes a recommendation of who is to do what, when he is to do it, and how he is to do it.

After reading the summary, about half of the managers said they might decide to refer the matter to a member of their staff to follow through. Those who read further said that they expect the introduction and background sections to give them the technical and chronological information necessary to follow the discussion. They also read the conclusions and recommendations, especially if these are not adequately stated in the summary. Their purpose in reading further is to gain a better perspective of the information reported and to find the answer to the question: *What do we do next?*

Of those who read the introduction and background sections, a portion said they also read the body of the report, where they expect to find the detailed discussion of the results. They read the body for one or more of four reasons: (1) they are especially interested in the subject; (2) they are deeply involved in the study; (3) the urgency of the study requires it; or (4) they were skeptical of the conclusions drawn.

A well-organized technical report resembles a well-organized newspaper story in many respects. Just as the opening or lead paragraph of the newspaper story tells the reader who did what, when, where, and how, so also must the opening summary of the technical report tell the reader what the report is about, what it contributes, what conclusions were reached, what recommendations are being made, and what actions are called for. And just as the newspaper story goes from the general to the specific, so too must the technical report; but not until the who, what, when, where, and how questions have been satisfied.

You must never forget that the technical report must be written from the reader's—and not the writer's—point of view. You should therefore be guided in your organization by these three questions:

1. Who's going to read the report?
2. What is the reader's background?
   and
3. What will he be looking for?

Once you have completed the investigation, it is not easy for you to discard the habits of an engineer and replace them with the habits of an author. Looking at data from the engineering point of view is often not the same as looking at it from the management point of view. Yet, this is exactly what you must do if the report is to be a worthwhile decision-making instrument. It is why the organization of the investigation, and of the report of the investigation, will almost always be in diametric opposition.

There is, of course, no one way to write a report, just as there is no one way to design a product. Except for standardized periodic reports, each report presents a design problem of its own. Thus, if you will extend your analytical approach to your writing problem, you are certain to produce more effective reports.

However, should you organize and write your report in the same way that you carried out the investigation—chronologically —you may be in trouble. Regrettably, many good scientists and engineers are guilty of this practice. For some unexplained reason, they believe the reader must experience the actual step-by-step procedures of the study—including, of course, the false leads and dead ends—to get a feel for the work. Although this may be good laboratory practice, and certainly such a report makes a good "whodunit," it's bad reporting procedure.

Level of Presentation

An aspect of report writing procedure that receives far too little attention is the technical level of presentation—the communications aspects of language. Trite as it may sound, the technical level and detail at which a report should be written depends upon the reader and his use of the material. Most readers—and certainly this is true for management readers—are interested in the significant material and in the general concepts that grow out of the detail. Consequently, there is seldom real justification for a highly technical and detailed presentation.

Usually the management reader has an education and experience background different from that of the writer. *Rarely* does the management reader have the same knowledge and familiarity with the specific problem being reported that the writer has. *Therefore, the writer of a report for management should write for a reader whose educational and experience background is in a field different from his own.* For example, if the report writer is an electrical engineer, he should write his report for a person educated and trained in some other discipline, not electrical engineering.

If the report is to convey information effectively, all parts of it *should preferably* be written at the level of articles published in the Westinghouse ENGINEER.* And, all parts of the report, other than

* The Souther paper (footnote 5, Chapter 2) specifies the *Scientific American* level. Westinghouse ENGINEER is edited on the same level.—Ed.

the body and appendix, *must* be written at the Westinghouse ENGINEER level. The highly technical, mathematical, and detailed material—if necessary—can and should be placed in the appendix.

The Role of Supervision in Report Writing

It is the responsibility of each supervisor to make sure each engineer under his direction knows *what his report is to do, how it is to be used, who is going to use it,* and *what decisions will be based on it.* The purpose is to increase the effectiveness of technical reports, both written and oral, by:

1. Seeing that the employe understands management's information needs;
2. Making the employe aware of the role his report plays and, therefore, the necessity for effective reporting; and
3. Increasing the employe's understanding of the relationship of his own work to that of other employes and to the goals of the Company.

The supervisor should also give the engineer the information and perspective he needs to communicate effectively. It is his responsibility to:

1. Define the project and the required reports;
2. Provide proper perspective to the required reporting; and
3. See that effective reports are submitted on time.

An effective report, like any engineered product, has to be designed to fill a particular need and to achieve a particular purpose within a specific situation. Thus, a logical starting point is to look at the needs of management readers.

Summary

The things-to-do that are suggested in this guide can save you valuable time. They will, if put to use, assure reports with a greater perspective and usefulness because these will be reflecting the experience and perspective of your supervisor. Another thing they'll do—they'll make it easier for you to get reports in on time because you'll have a clear idea of the kind of information management wants in technical reports; and perhaps equally important, a clear idea of the kind of information management doesn't want in reports. And finally, the intent of the guide is to focus your attention on the content aspect, rather than the structuring aspect, of report writing.

APPLICATIONS

1. Some management men blame English departments of colleges and universities for ineffective writing done by science and engineering graduates. Do you think this is a fair criticism? To what extent? Write a summary of the role you think management should take in providing a favorable climate for upward communication within a company.

2. Choose a paper, report, or thesis that you have already written, and criticize it over *all* the guidelines set forth in "What to Report."

3. Plan your next paper *in detail* in the light of these same principles.

4 | Order Out of Chaos

When Irving Stone addressed a meeting of the California Writers' Club not long ago, he had already written *Lust for Life* and fifteen other books. He said that it was not until he was working on his seventeenth, *The Agony and the Ecstasy,* that he *fully* realized the importance of structure in planning any piece of writing. For the scientist or engineer who—unaware of the implications of such a professional attitude for his own work—"just sits down and writes," a study of the methods of structuring a report is a must.

In fact, he may expect that study of organization will challenge his best efforts throughout his writing life. Only a year before he died, Charles Darwin summed up the problems of organization in these human words:

I have as much difficulty as ever in expressing myself clearly and concisely; and this difficulty has caused me a very great loss of time; but it has had the compensating advantage of forcing me to think long and intently about every sentence, and thus I have been led to see errors in reasoning and in my own observations or those of others.

There seems to be a sort of fatality in my mind leading me to put at first my statement or proposition in a wrong or awkward form. Formerly I used to think about my sentences before writing them down; but for several years I have found that it saves time to scribble in a vile hand whole pages as quickly as I possibly can, contracting half the words; and then correct deliberately. Sentences thus scribbled down are often better ones than I could have written deliberately.

Having said thus much about my manner of writing, I will add that with my large books I spend a good deal of time over the general arrangement of the matter. I first make the rudest outline in two or three pages, and then a larger one in several pages, a few words or one word standing for a whole discussion or series of facts. Each one of these headings is again enlarged and often transferred before I begin to write *in extenso*. As in several of my books facts observed by others have been very extensively used, and as I have always had several quite distinct subjects in hand at the same time, I may mention that I keep from thirty to forty large portfolios, in cabinets with labeled shelves, into which I can at once put a detached reference or memorandum. I have bought many books, and at their ends I make an index of all the facts that concern my work; or, if the book is not my own, write out a separate abstract, and of such abstracts I have a large drawer full. Before beginning on any subject I look to all the short indexes and make a general and classified index, and by taking the one or more proper portfolios I have all the information collected during my life ready for use.[1]

Although few writers will ever need to review a lifetime collection to organize any particular piece, Darwin's method is an effective way to organize anything—from a short memorandum to a long book.

Perhaps the commonest situation that faces the scientist or engineer is that in which he must build a tight, streamlined report from bits and pieces of laboratory notebooks, chronological reports, analytical and testing laboratory reports, literature refer-

[1] Francis Darwin, ed., *The Life and Letters of Charles Darwin* (New York: Appleton, 1889), pp. 79–80.

ences, discussion notes, patent citations, technical correspondence, and many others—all in a chaotic jumble of disorganization. His problem is to float the mineral from the gangue and to refine the concentrate in such a way as to lead the reader by the shortest path to the information he needs.

The writer's best strategy is to build a good outline. This is a powerful aid in deciding on the elements that are essential to the report and in fixing the logical relationships among them. It is also an efficient procedure for arriving at the key idea of the report. John E. Jordan has cogently put it:

> An outline is in part a pious statement of intention, in part a skeleton to flesh out, in part a blueprint to follow, in part a cut-down model on which to try out ideas. It is not, except under unusual circumstances, a deep freeze to preserve bits of prime verbiage for later embellishment of the finished work. If you think of an outline as a skeleton upon which to build up a structure—like a sculptor's armature for supporting and directing the shape of a clay statue—you might remember that a skeleton does not show through except in cases of emaciation. Yet bone structure is of fundamental importance, none the less. If you think of an outline as an architect's drawing, you might remember that even architects make mistakes and very few buildings are put up without some changes in plan during construction. An outline is not a strait jacket, it is a tool; its only real requirement is that it be useful.[2]

In practice, there are four kinds of outlines. These are the *scratch outline,* the *topic outline,* the *sentence outline,* and the *paragraph outline.*

The Scratch Outline

A scratch outline is of the sort that you might put on the back of an old envelope. It consists simply of random notes and jottings— often mere words or phrases, set down in no particular order—to remind you of the points you want to write about. For a short technical memorandum, a scratch outline may be all you will need. Having noted all your points, you should then review them to fix the best order of presentation. Your first point may be two-thirds of the way down your list. No matter. Number it "1." Your second

2 John E. Jordan, *Using Rhetoric* (New York: Harper & Row, 1965), pp. 105–106.

point may head the list; number it "2." After you have numbered all your points and perhaps added some and crossed out a few as not worth bothering with, you are ready to write your short piece. As simple as this sounds, it is far more efficient than "just sitting down to write."

A scratch outline such as might have been used by W. I. B. Beveridge in working out his article "Reason," which follows this chapter, might look like this:

REASON

10—Unverified assumptions creep

 4—Extreme view

21—"Facts"

15—Value of report writing for research worker

 1—Limitations and hazards

12—Generalizations disprovable—but not provable

 6—Deduction

18—Penicillin

 2—Bacon quote

20—Rats

13—"Folklore" of the open mind

 8—Definition

 3—Proof

17—Vitamins

 7—Induction

 5—Reason has poor record

 9—Safeguards

16—Hughlings Jackson

19—Cause and effect

11—Arguing to the future

14—Extrapolation: danger!

These, as you see, are the briefest of notes to remind the writer of the points he wants to deal with, jotted down just as they occur to him. If you rearrange the list so that the numbered points are in order from 1 to 21, you will see that they fall in the order in which Beveridge takes them up in his paper.

Besides its use for short pieces, the scratch outline is also a helpful preliminary to preparing the more detailed outlines that are most useful for organizing longer reports and articles.

The Topic Outline

If your report is to be of some length or complexity, you should turn a preliminary scratch outline into either a topic outline or a sentence outline. These two kinds of outlines show at a glance the logical arrangement of the elements of the report. The items from a scratch outline may be conveniently rearranged under a conventional system of symbols, such as:

I., II., etc., to mark the main points

A., B., etc., for the subpoints under these

1., 2., etc., for the subpoints under A. and B.

And so on, through a., (1), (a), and (i), as may be needed. For example, a brief topic outline of an address by Dr. Philip Sporn, "Vision and Synthesis in Engineering,"[3] might look somewhat as follows:

Vision and Synthesis in Engineering

   I. Vision a prelude to synthesis
      A. Vision and the possible
      B. Synthesis and reality
  II. Synthesis defined
      A. Meets national needs
      B. Meets social needs
      C. Meets economic needs
 III. Anatomy of vision and synthesis
      A. Series of closely related steps
      B. Execution of successful synthesis
 IV. Examples of vision and synthesis
      A. Ultrarapid closure of power transmission lines
         1. Early circuit interrupting devices

[3] The second in a series of six lectures delivered in the spring of 1963 at the Cornell College of Engineering by Dr. Philip Sporn, formerly president and now chairman of the System Development Committee, American Electric Power Company, Inc. The lecture series has been published in book form (*Foundations of Engineering* [New York: Pergamon, 1964]) and will amply repay study as a model of clear presentation of engineering philosophy and practice.

    2. Analysis of relay problems
    3. Deionizing characteristics of air
    4. Synthesis
    5. Performance now near-perfect
  B. Portsmouth gaseous diffusion plant
    1. Magnitude of power problems
    2. Advanced concepts of power generation
    3. Cost considerations
    4. Critical problems
    5. Formal proposal
V. Test of successful synthesis
  A. Project ahead of schedule—under budget
  B. Recent power costs
VI. Good examples of vision and synthesis in engineering

The Sentence Outline

The foregoing topic outline is offered here for illustrative purposes only. For a presentation as complex as Sporn's, a full sentence outline would be more appropriate. In such an outline, each point is developed as a full sentence, each sentence being as precise and expressive as the writer can make it. Vague statements have no place here. It is here that the writer comes to close grips with his subject, and clean, sharp statement is essential both to good overall organization and to efficient writing in the later stages.

As early as possible in the preparation of an outline, a *thesis statement* should be crystallized. This is a well-rounded expression —in a single sentence—of the key idea of the presentation. It answers the *key question* that the report sets out to deal with.

For example, one industrial survey report compared the salaries of scientists and engineers in prominent American research and development organizations. The key question—to which management wanted the answer—was: "Is Company X paying its research men enough money?" After completion of the survey and review of the findings, a thesis statement could be put in the following form: "The incomes of the scientists and engineers in Company X are competitive with the national average when all fringe benefits are included, but the net take-home salary level is below the national average."

After formulation of such a thesis statement, the writer should then proceed to tighten his outline by checking to see that every sentence drives toward and supports the thesis statement and that every irrelevant point is ruthlessly thrown out. Even at this stage, however, you should not think of your outline as precast to harden like concrete. Think of it as subject to whatever changes—to use Darwin's phrase—your writing *in extenso* may suggest.

As an example, the first part of a sentence outline for a magazine article follows. It is not offered as a perfect model, but rather as a typical specimen. After you have looked it over, take time to consider ways in which you think it might be improved.

The New Biology: Cockroaches and Cancer

Thesis statement: Recent fundamental research on common cockroaches may lead medical scientists to a better understanding of the causes of cancer.

I. Last December, the President's Commission on Heart Disease, Cancer and Stroke predicted that 830,000 Americans would be under treatment for cancer in 1964.
   A. The committee urgently recommended a step-up in biomedical research.
II. Exciting new ideas for the direction of such research have been developed since World War II.
   A. These ideas are based on the hypothesis that all organisms possess living clocks.
      1. Janet Harker showed that upsetting these clocks led to cancer in cockroaches.
      2. German workers found that the effects of cancer-producing chemicals depend on the time of day they are applied.
III. Man has observed simple periodicities in plants and animals from the earliest times.
   A. Jean de Mairan discovered (1729) that the leaves of the sensitive plant wake at dawn and fold at night.
   B. The periodic phosphorescence of a seaworm was probably the flickering light that Columbus saw as he approached the New World.

And so on. The complete outline ran to some three pages and was of much help in writing the final article. As we show, however, it might also have served another very useful purpose.

The Paragraph Outline

A fourth kind of outline, while not best suited as a prelude to writing, is helpful in studying the structure of models of good writing. This is called the paragraph outline. It consists simply of the topic sentences of each paragraph arranged in the order of their presentation. A topic sentence as written may not be fully expressive of the paragraph idea, and in that case it should be rewritten. Or, a topic sentence may be implied rather than directly stated. In that case, an explicit one should be written out.

Revising Outlines

Besides helping to clarify your own ideas, a sentence outline can save time in another way. If you will discuss your outline with whoever will approve your report—your instructor, your thesis committee chairman, or your supervisor—and revise it in line with the suggestions you are sure to get, you can be confident that the paper you write from it will be well received.

The magazine article "The New Biology," cited earlier, will serve as an example of how time can be wasted by writing a finished piece before discussing the outline with a superior. In this case the editor had expressed enthusiasm about the subject matter, and the writer wrote the article and submitted it without further ado.

After reading the finished piece, the editor replied as follows:

Y'S MAGAZINE, LTD.[4]
711 Thirteenth Street
New York, New York

Editorial Rooms   *April 1, 1967*

DEAR MR. QUILL:

As [our assistant editor] has told you, we find Dr. Harker's research fascinating and think your report on it will make an excellent piece for Y'S MAGAZINE. We will be glad, in due course, to do a little

---

[4] The names are fictitious; otherwise, this is an authentic letter.

editorial tinkering with your manuscript. But before we get to that stage we hope you will undertake some revisions in the light of the following comments:

1. The lead and conclusion are distracting. This should be simply a report on Dr. Harker's work and its significance, not an appeal for overall support for basic research in general. A straightforward, direct opening would probably be better. Perhaps you might begin at the point I have marked at the bottom of page 3.

2. The historical material on pages 4 through 7 is good, but it should be deferred until you have drawn a clear picture of Dr. Harker and her experiments.

3. We think you should drop the personal material about Dr. Harker on pages 7 and 8 or boil it down to a sentence or two.

4. Why did interest in biological clocks increase after World War II? Dr. Harker's answer is not very illuminating (I have marked other places where scientific jargon should also be cut or paraphrased). Was it because of interest in war workers on swing shift?

5. We hope you will add some more material on studies of stress and biological clocks in humans. How do people react to shifts in their sleep-waking schedules? It seems to me that I have seen some studies of this on policemen and others. A paragraph or two on the subject would be interesting.

6. Can you cite studies on the connection between cancer and stress in human beings or other animals? You introduce this thought very casually, in a single sentence on page 15. And the Cloudsley-Thompson quote that follows is more sonorous than informative.

7. Elsewhere, I think you have overused direct quotes. I would limit these to statements like "It was a rather fiddling task" (page 13) which gives a vivid sense of her personality. Elsewhere if the quote is just straight exposition, it could probably be said more briefly and clearly by the author.

I hope some of these suggestions seem reasonable to you and that you will send us a revised manuscript at an early date.

Sincerely,
s/ MERDER ROWE
EDITOR

Some of these comments could have been made only after the editor had read the finished article, but he also found much that he thought was structurally wrong with it. The time that the writer could have saved if he had first submitted a full outline is too obvious to need comment. A similar situation is highly probable in the relationship between the technical writer and his superior. Even between two individuals good communication leading to mutual understanding is hard to come by, as many marriages attest.

When to Outline

The most efficient and effective way to work up an outline for a technical report is to jot down notes from time to time as your laboratory or design work progresses. If you do this regularly, your outline will almost build itself. Your final structuring and re-arrangement will then be relatively easy, and you can sit down to draft your report with confidence and an uncluttered mind.

A technical report can be looked at as a small slice of history, and a glance at the historian's method may be helpful here. Edward Hallett Carr described his own way of working in a noted lecture:

Laymen—that is to say, non-academic friends or friends from other disciplines—sometimes ask me how the historian goes to work when he writes history. The commonest assumption appears to be that the historian divides his work into two sharply distinguishable phases or periods. First, he spends a long preliminary period reading his sources and filling his notebooks with facts: then, when this is over, he puts away his sources, takes out his notebooks, and writes his book from beginning to end. This is to me an unconvincing and unplausible picture. For myself, as soon as I have got going on a few of what I take to be the capital sources, the itch becomes too strong and I begin to write—not necessarily at the beginning, but somewhere, anywhere. Thereafter, reading and writing go simultaneously. The writing is added to, subtracted from, reshaped, cancelled, as I go on reading. The reading is guided and directed and made fruitful by the writing: the more I write, the more I know what I am looking for, the better I understand the significance and relevance of what I find. Some historians probably do all this preliminary writing in their heads without using pen, paper, or typewriter, just as some people play chess in their heads without recourse to board and chess-men: this is a talent which I envy, but cannot emulate. But I am convinced that, for any historian worth the name, the two processes of what economists call "input" and "output" go on simultaneously and are, in practice, parts of a single process. If you try to separate them, or to give one priority over the other, you fall into one of two heresies. Either you write scissors-and-paste history without meaning or significance; or you write propaganda or historical fiction, and merely use facts of the past to embroider a kind of writing that has nothing to do with history.[5]

It is not suggested that an engineer or scientist attempt to write his actual report as his work is in progress—only that he make notes for his outline. If he approaches his writing problems in this way, he may borrow from the historian's method to good advantage.

The Parts of a Technical Report

Rudyard Kipling wrote:

> There are nine and sixty ways of
> constructing tribal lays,
> And every single one of them is
> right.[6]

In much the same way, every company and every government agency whose reports you may have opportunity to study, or for which you may write, probably uses a somewhat different format for its technical reports. This is of no particular importance. Such details can be quickly learned as they are needed. Thus no purpose would be served in suggesting any particular format here. Any report that is basically well organized can be tailored to fit whatever scheme an organization has adopted as standard.

The following most common report elements may, however, serve as a useful check list.

5 Edward Hallett Carr, *What Is History?* (New York: Knopf, 1965), pp. 32–33.
6 From "In the Neolithic Age," in *Rudyard Kipling's Verse* (New York: Doubleday, 1928).

Letter of transmittal
Cover
Title page
Abstract or summary
Table of contents
List of tables, charts, and
   illustrations
Definitions and explanation
   of symbols

Report proper
   Introduction
   Development section, or body
   Recommendations and conclusions
Appendix
Bibliography
Index
Distribution List

Reason

W. I. B. Beveridge

W. I. B. Beveridge was educated at Cranbrook School, St. Paul's College, University of Sydney, and holds an M.A. from Cambridge. He is professor of animal pathology at Cambridge and a fellow at Jesus College. According to The New York Times, *"Many of the author's statements deserve to be quoted in every treatise on the psychology and practice of research."*

Discovery should come as an adventure rather than as the result of a logical process of thought. Sharp, prolonged thinking is necessary that we may keep to the chosen road, but it does not necessarily lead to discovery.

—THEOBALD SMITH

Limitations and Hazards

Before considering the rôle of reason in research it may be useful to discuss the limitations of reason. These are more serious than most people realize, because our conception of science has been given us by teachers and authors who have presented science in logical arrangement and that is seldom the way in which knowledge is actually acquired.

Everyday experience and history teach us that in the biological and medical sciences reason seldom can progress far from the facts without going astray. The scholasticism and authoritarianism prevailing during the Middle Ages [were] incompatible with science. With the Renaissance came a change in outlook: the belief that things ought and must behave according to accepted views (mostly taken from the classics) was supplanted by a desire to observe things as they really are, and human knowledge began to grow again. Francis Bacon had a great influence on the development of science mainly, I think, because he showed that most discoveries had been made empirically rather than by use of deductive logic. In 1605 he said:

Men are rather beholden . . . generally to chance or anything else, than to logic, for the invention of arts and sciences. (1),

and in 1620,

the present system of logic rather assists in confirming and rendering inveterate the errors founded on vulgar notions, than in searching after truth, and is therefore more hurtful than useful. (2).

Later the French philosopher René Descartes made people realize that reason can land us in endless fallacies. His golden rule was:

Give unqualified assent to no propositions but those the truth of which is so clear and distinct that they cannot be doubted.

Every child, indeed one might even say, every young vertebrate, discovers gravity; and yet modern science with all its knowledge cannot yet satisfactorily "explain" it. Not only are reason and logic therefore insufficient to provide a means of discovering gravity without empirical knowledge of it, but all the reason and logic applied in classical times did not even enable intelligent men to deduce correctly the elementary facts concerning it.

F. C. S. Schiller, a modern philosopher, has made some

illuminating comments on the use of logic in science and I shall quote from him at length:

Among the obstacles to scientific progress a high place must certainly be assigned to the analysis of scientific procedure which logic has provided. . . . It has not tried to describe the methods by which the sciences have actually advanced, and to extract . . . rules which might be used to regulate scientific progress, but has freely re-arranged the actual procedure in accordance with its prejudices, for the order of discovery there has been substituted an order of proof. (3).

Credence of the logician's view has been encouraged by the method generally adopted in the writing of scientific papers. The logical presentation of results which is usually followed is hardly ever a chronological or full account of how the investigation was actually carried out, for such would often be dull and difficult to follow and, for ordinary purposes, wasteful of space. In his book on the writing of scientific papers, Allbutt specifically advocates that the course of the research should not be followed but that a deductive presentation should be adopted.

To quote again from Schiller, who takes an extreme view:

It is not too much to say that the more deference men of science have paid to logic, the worse it has been for the scientific value of their reasoning. . . . Fortunately for the world, however, the great men of science have usually been kept in salutary ignorance of the logical tradition. (3).

He goes on to say that logic was developed to regulate debates in the Greek schools, assemblies and law-courts. It was necessary to determine which side won, and logic served this purpose, but it should not occasion surprise that it is quite unsuitable in science, for which it was never intended. Many logicians emphatically declare that logic, interested in correctness and validity, has nothing at all to do with productive thinking.

Schiller goes even further in his criticism of traditional logic and says that not only is it of little value in making new discoveries, but that history has shown it to be of little value in recognising their validity or ensuring their acceptance when they have been proclaimed. Indeed, logical reasoning has often prevented the acceptance of new truths, as is illustrated by the persecution to which the great discoverers have so often been subjected.

The slowness and difficulty with which the human race makes discoveries and its blindness to the most obvious facts, if it happens to be unprepared or unwilling to see them, should suffice to show that there is something gravely wrong about the logician's account of discovery.

Schiller was protesting mainly against the view of the scientific method expounded by certain logicians in the latter half of the nineteenth century. Most modern philosophers concerning themselves with the scientific method do not interpret this phrase as including the art of discovery, which they consider to be outside their province. They are interested in the philosophical implications of science.

Wilfred Trotter (4) also had some provocative things to say about the poor record which reason has in the advancement of scientific knowledge. Not only has it few discoveries to its credit compared to empiricism, he says, but often reason has obstructed the advance of science owing to false doctrines based on it. In medicine particularly, practices founded on reason alone have often prevailed for years or centuries before someone with an independent mind questioned them and in many cases showed they were more harmful than beneficial.

Logicians distinguish between inductive reasoning (from particular instances to general principles, from facts to theories) and deductive reasoning (from the general to the particular, applying a theory to a particular case). In induction one starts from observed data and develops a generalisation which explains the relationships · between the objects observed. On the other hand, in deductive reasoning one starts from some general law and applies it to a particular instance. Thus in deductive reasoning the derived conclusion is contained within the original premiss, and should be true if the premiss is true.

Since deduction consists of applying general principles to further instances, it cannot lead us to new generalisations and so cannot give rise to major advances in science. On the other hand the inductive process is at the same time less trustworthy but more productive. It is more productive because it is a means of arriving at new theories, but is less trustworthy because starting from a collection of facts we can often infer several possible theories, all of which cannot be true as some may be mutually incompatible; indeed none of them may be true.

In biology every phenomenon and circumstance is so complex and so poorly understood that premisses are not clear-cut and hence reasoning is unreliable. Nature is often too subtle for our reasoning. In mathematics, physics and chemistry the basic premisses are more firmly established and the attendant circumstances can be more rigidly defined and controlled. Therefore reason plays a rather more dominant part in extending knowledge in these sciences. Nevertheless the mathematician Poincaré said: "Logic has very little to do with discovery or invention." Similar views were expressed by Planck and Einstein (5, 6). The point here is that inductions are usually arrived at not by the mechanical application of logic but by intuition, and the course of our thoughts is constantly guided by our personal judgment. On the other hand the logician is not concerned with the way the mind functions but with logical formulation.

From his experience in finding that his hypotheses always had to be abandoned or at least greatly modified Darwin learnt to distrust deductive reasoning in the biological sciences. He said:

I must begin with a good body of facts, and not from principle, in which I always suspect some fallacy. (7).

A basic difficulty in applying reason in research derives from the fact that terms often cannot be defined accurately and premisses are seldom precise or unconditionally true. Especially in biology premisses are only true under certain circumstances. For careful reasoning and clarity of thought one should first define the terms one uses but in biology exact definitions are often difficult or impossible to arrive at. Take, for example, the statement "influenza is caused by a virus." Influenza was originally a clinical concept, that is to say, a disease defined on clinical characters. We now know that diseases caused by several different microbes have been embraced by what the clinician regards as influenza. The virus worker would now prefer to define influenza as a disease caused by a virus with certain characters. But this only passes on the difficulty to the defining of an influenza virus which in turn escapes precise definition.

These difficulties are to some extent resolved if we accept the principle that in all our reasoning we can deal only in probabilities. Indeed much of our reasoning in biology is more aptly termed speculation.

I have mentioned some limitations inherent in the application of logical processes in science; another common source of error is incorrect reasoning, such as committing some logical fallacy. It is a delusion that the use of reason is easy and needs no training or special caution. In the following section I have tried to outline some general precautions which it may be helpful to keep in mind in using reason in research.

Some Safeguards in Use of Reason in Research

The first consideration is to examine the basis from which we start reasoning. This involves arriving at as clear an understanding as possible of what we mean by the terms we employ, and examining our premises. Some of the premises may be well-established facts or laws, while others may be purely suppositions. It is often necessary to admit provisionally some assumptions that are not well established, in which case one needs to be careful not to forget that they are only suppositions. Michael Faraday warned against the tendency of the mind "to rest on an assumption" and when it appears to fit in with other knowledge to forget that it has not been proved. It is generally agreed that unverified assumptions should be kept down to a bare minimum and the hypothesis with the fewest assumptions is to be preferred. (This is known as the maxim of parsimony, or "Occam's Razor." It was propounded by William of Occam in the fourteenth century.)

How easy it is for unverified assumptions to creep into our reasoning unnoticed! They are often introduced by expressions such as "obviously," "of course," "surely." I would have thought that it was a fairly safe assumption that well-fed animals live longer on the average than underfed ones, but in recent experiments mice whose diet was restricted to a point where their growth rate was below normal lived much longer than mice allowed to eat as much as they wished.

Having arrived at a clear understanding of the basis from which we start, at every step in our reasoning it is essential to pause and consider whether all conceivable alternatives have been taken into account. The degree of uncertainty or supposition is usually greatly magnified at each step.

It is important not to confuse facts with their interpretations, that is to say, to distinguish between data and generalisations. Facts are particular observational data relating to the past or present. To take an obvious illustration: it may be a fact that when a certain drug was administered to rabbits it killed them, but to say that the drug is poisonous for rabbits is not a statement of fact but a generalisation or law arrived at by induction. The change from the past tense to the present usually involves stepping from the facts to the induction. It is a step which must often be taken but only with an understanding of what one is doing. Confusion may also arise from the way in which results are interpreted: strictly the facts arising from experiments can only be described by a precise statement of what occurred. Often in describing an experiment we interpret the results into other terms, perhaps without realising we are departing from a statement of the facts.

A difficulty we are always up against is that we have to argue from past and present to the future. Science, to be of value, must predict. We have to reason from data obtained in the past by experiment and observation, and plan accordingly for the future. This presents special difficulties in biology because, owing to the incompleteness of our knowledge, we can seldom be sure that changed circumstances in the future may not influence the results. Take, for example, the testing of a new vaccine against a disease. The vaccine may prove effective in several experiments but we must still be cautious in saying it will be effective in future. Influenza vaccine gave a considerable degree of protection in large scale trials in U.S.A. in 1943 and 1945, but against the next epidemic in 1947 it was of no value. Regarded as a problem in logic the position is that by inductive inference from our data we arrive at a generalisation (for instance, that the vaccine is effective). Then in future when we wish to guard against the disease we use this generalisation deductively and apply it to the particular practical problem of protecting certain people. The difficult point in the reasoning is, of course, making the induction. Logic has little to say here that is of help to us. All we can do is to refrain from generalising until we have collected fairly extensive data to provide a wide basis for the induction and regard as tentative any conclusion based on induction, or, as we more often hear in everyday language, be cautious with generalisations. Statistics help us in drawing conclusions from our data by ensuring that our conclusions have a certain reliability, but even statistical conclusions are strictly valid only for events which have already occurred.

Generalisations can never be *proved*. They can be tested by seeing whether deductions made from them are in accord with experimental and observational facts, and if the results are not as predicted, the hypothesis or generalisation may be *disproved*. But a favourable result does not prove the generalisation, because the deduction made from it may be true without its being true. Deductions, themselves correct, may be made from palpably absurd generalisations. For instance, the truth of the hypothesis that plague is due to evil spirits is not established by the correctness of the deduction that you can avoid the disease by keeping out of the reach of the evil spirits. In strict logic a generalisation is never proved and remains on probation indefinitely, but if it survives all attempts at disproof it is accepted in practice, especially if it fits well into a wider theoretical scheme.

If scientific logic shows we must be cautious in arriving at generalisations ourselves, it shows for the same reasons that we should not place excessive trust in any generalisation, even widely accepted theories or laws. Newton did not regard the laws he formulated as the ultimate truth, but probably most following him did until Einstein showed how well-founded Newton's caution had been. In less fundamental matters how often do we see widely accepted notions superseded!

Therefore the scientist cannot afford to allow his mind to become fixed, with reference not only to his own opinions but also to prevailing ideas. Theobald Smith said:

Research is fundamentally a state of mind involving continual re-examination of doctrines and axioms upon which current thought and action are based. It is, therefore, critical of existing practices.(8).

No accepted idea or "established principle" should be regarded as beyond being questioned if there is an observation challenging it. Bernard wrote:

If an idea presents itself to us, we must not reject it simply because it does not agree with the logical deductions of a reigning theory.

Great discoveries have been made by means of experiments devised with complete disregard for well accepted beliefs. Evidently it was Darwin who introduced the expression "fool's experiment" to refer to such experiments, which he often undertook to test what most people would consider not worth testing.

People in most other walks of life can allow themselves the indulgence of fixed ideas and prejudices which make thinking so much easier, and for all of us it is a practical necessity to hold definite opinions on many issues in everyday life, but the research worker must try to keep his mind malleable and avoid holding set ideas in science. We have to strive to keep our mind receptive and to examine suggestions made by others fairly and on their own merits, seeking arguments for as well as against them. We must be critical, certainly, but beware lest ideas be rejected because an automatic reaction causes us to see only the arguments against them. We tend to resist ideas competing with our own.

A useful habit for scientists to develop is that of not trusting ideas based on reason only. As Trotter says, they come into the mind often with a disarming air of obviousness and certainty. Some consider that there is no such thing as pure reasoning, that is to say, except where mathematical symbols are involved. Practically all reasoning is influenced by feelings, prejudice and past experience, albeit often subconsciously. Trotter wrote:

The dispassionate intellect, the open mind, the unprejudiced observer, exist in an exact sense only in a sort of intellectualist folk-lore; states even approaching them cannot be reached without a moral and emotional effort most of us cannot or will not make.

A trick of the mind well known to psychologists is to "rationalise," that is, to justify by reasoned argument a view which in reality is determined by preconceived judgment in the subconscious mind, the latter being governed by self-interest, emotional considerations, instinct, prejudice and similar factors which the person usually does not realise or admit even to himself. In somewhat similar vein is W. H. George's warning against believing that things in nature ought to conform to certain patterns or standards and regarding all exceptions as abnormal. He says that the "should-ought mechanism" has no place whatever in research, and its complete abandonment is one of the foundation stones of science. It is premature, he considers, to worry about the technique of experimentation until a man has become dissatisfied with the "should-ought" way of thinking.

It has been said by some that scientists should train themselves to adopt a disinterested attitude to their work. I cannot agree with this view and think the investigator should try to exercise sufficient self-control to consider fairly the evidence against a certain outcome for which he fervently hopes, rather than to try to be disinterested. It is better to recognise and face the danger that our reasoning may be influenced by our wishes. Also it is unwise to deny ourselves the pleasure of associating ourselves wholeheartedly with our ideas, for to do so would be to undermine one of the chief incentives in science.

It is important to distinguish between interpolation and extrapolation. Interpolating means filling in a gap *between* established facts which form a series. When one draws a curve on a graph by connecting the points one interpolates. Extrapolating is going *beyond* a series of observations on the assumption that the same trend continues. Interpolation is considered permissible for most purposes provided one has a good series of data to work from, but extrapolation is much more hazardous. Apparently obvious extensions of our theories beyond the field in which they have been tested often lead us astray. The process of extrapolation is rather similar to implication and is useful in providing suggestions.

A useful aid in getting a clear understanding of a problem is to write a report on all the information available. This is helpful when one is starting an investigation, when up against a difficulty, or when the investigation is nearing completion. Also at the beginning of an investigation it is useful to set out clearly the questions for which an answer is being sought. Stating the problem precisely sometimes takes one a long way toward the solution. The systematic arrangement of the data often discloses flaws in the reasoning, or alternative lines of thought which had been missed. Assumptions and conclusions at first accepted as "obvious" may even prove indefensible when set down clearly and examined critically. Some institutions make it a rule for all research workers to furnish a report quarterly on the work done, and work planned. This is useful not only for the director to keep in touch with developments but also to the workers themselves. Certain directors prefer verbal reports which they consider more useful in helping the research worker "get his ideas straight."

Careful and correct use of language is a powerful aid to straight thinking, for putting into words precisely what we mean necessitates getting our own minds quite clear on what we mean. It is with words that we do our reasoning, and writing is the expression of our thinking. Discipline and training in writing is probably the best training there is in reasoning. Allbutt has said that slovenly writing reflects slovenly thinking, and obscure writing usually confused thinking. The main aim in scientific reports is to be as clear and precise as possible and make each sentence mean exactly what it is intended to and be incapable of other interpretation. Words or phrases that do not have an exact meaning are to be avoided because once one has given a name to something, one immediately has a feeling that the position has been clarified, whereas often the contrary is true. "A verbal cloak of ignorance is a garment that often hinders progress."(9).

The Rôle of Reason in Research

Although discoveries originate more often from unexpected experimental results or observations, or from intuitions, than directly from logical thought, reason is the [principal] agent in most other aspects of research and the guide to most of our actions. It is the main tool in formulating hypotheses, in judging the correctness of ideas conjured up by imagination and intuition, in planning experiments and deciding what observations to make, in assessing the evidence and interpreting new facts, in making generalisations and finally in finding extensions and applications of a discovery.

The methods and functions of discovery and proof in research are as different as are those of a detective and of a judge in a court of law. While playing the part of the detective the investigator follows clues, but having captured his alleged fact, he turns judge and examines the case by means of logically arranged evidence. Both functions are equally essential but they are different.

It is in "factual" discoveries in biology that observation and chance—empiricism—plays such an important part. But facts obtained by observation or experiment usually only gain significance when we use reason to build them into the general body of knowledge. Darwin said:

Science consists in grouping facts so that general laws or conclusions may be drawn from them. (7).

In research it is not sufficient to collect facts; by interpreting them, by seeing their significance and consequences we can often go much further. Walshe considers that just as important as making discoveries is what we make *of* our discoveries, or for that matter, of those of other people (10). To help retain and use information our minds require a rationalised, logically consistent body of knowledge. Hughlings Jackson said that

We have multitudes of facts, but we require, as they accumulate, organisation of them into higher knowledge; we require generalisations and working hypotheses.

The recognition of a new general principle is the consummation of scientific study.

Discoveries originating from so-called chance observations, from unexpected results in experiments or from intuitions are dramatic and arrest attention more than progress resulting from purely rational experimentation in which each step follows logically on the previous one so that the discovery only gradually unfolds. Therefore the latter, less spectacular process may be responsible for more advances than has been implied in the other chapters of this book. Moreover, as Zinsser said:

The preparatory accumulation of minor discoveries and of accurately observed details . . . is almost as important for the mobilisation of great forward drives as the periodic correlation of these disconnected observations into principles and laws by the vision of genius. (11).

Often when one looks into the origin of a discovery one finds that it was a much more gradual process than one had imagined.

In nutritional research, the discovery of the existence of the various vitamins was in a number of instances empirical, but subsequent development of knowledge of them was rational. Usually in chemotherapy, after the initial empirical discovery opening up the field, rational experimentation has led to a series of improvements, as in the development of sulphathiazole, sulphamerazine, sulphaguanidine, etc., following on the discovery of the therapeutic value of sulphanilamide, the first compound of this type found to have bacteriostatic properties.

. . . Fleming followed up a chance observation to discover that the mould *Penicillium notatum* produced a substance that had bacteriostatic properties and was non-toxic. However, he did not pursue it sufficiently to develop a chemotherapeutic agent and the investigation was dropped. During the latter quarter of the last century and first part of this there were literally dozens of reports of discoveries of antibacterial substances produced by bacteria and fungi (12). Even penicillin itself was discovered before Fleming or Florey (13). Quite a number of writers had not only suggested that these products might be useful therapeutically but had employed them and in some instances good results seem to have been obtained (12). But all these empirical discoveries were of little consequence until Florey, by a deliberately planned, systematic attack on the problem, produced penicillin in a relatively pure and stable form and so was able to demonstrate its great clinical value. Often the original discovery, like the crude ore from the mine, is of little value until it has been refined and fully developed. This latter process, less spectacular and largely rational, usually requires a different type of scientist and often a team. The rôle of reason in research is not so much in exploring the frontiers of knowledge as in developing the findings of the explorers.

A type of reasoning not yet mentioned is reasoning by analogy, which plays an important part in scientific thought. An analogy is a resemblance between the relationship of things, rather than between the things themselves. When one perceives that the relationship between A and B resembles the relationship between X and Y on one point, and one knows that A is related to B in various other ways, this suggests looking for similar relationships between X and Y. Analogy is very valuable in suggesting clues or hypotheses and in helping us comprehend phenomena and occurrences we cannot see. It is continually used in scientific thought and language but it is as well to keep in mind that analogy can often be quite misleading and of course can never prove anything.

Perhaps it is relevant to mention here that modern scientific philosophers try to avoid the notion of cause and effect. The current attitude is that scientific theories aim at describing associations between events without attempting to explain the relationship as being causal. The idea of cause, as implying an inherent necessity, raises philosophical difficulties and in theoretical physics the idea can be abandoned with advantage as there is then no longer the need to postulate a connection between the cause and effect. Thus, in this view, science confines itself to description—"how," not "why."

This outlook has been developed especially in relation to theoretical physics. In biology the concept of cause and effect is still used in practice, but when we speak of *the* cause of an event we are really over-simplifying a complex situation. Very many factors are involved in bringing about an event but in practice we commonly ignore or take for granted those that are always present or well-known and single out as *the* cause one factor which is unusual or which attracts our attention for a special reason. The cause of an outbreak of plague may be regarded by the bacteriologist as the microbe he finds in the blood of the victims, by the entomologist as the microbe-carrying fleas that spread the disease, by the epidemiologist as the rats that escaped from the ship and brought the infection into the port.

Summary

The origin of discoveries is beyond the reach of reason. The rôle of reason in research is not hitting on discoveries—either factual or theoretical—but verifying, interpreting and developing them and building a general theoretical scheme. Most biological "facts" and theories are only true under certain conditions and our knowledge is so incomplete that at best we can only reason on probabilities and possibilities.

References

1. Francis Bacon (1605). *The Advancement of Learning.*
2. ———— (1620). *Novum Organum.*
3. F. C. S. Schiller (1917). "Scientific Discovery and Logical Proof," in *Studies in the History and Method of Science,* edited by Charles Singer. Clarendon Press, Oxford. Permission to quote kindly granted by Clarendon Press, Oxford.
4. Wilfred Trotter (1941). *Collected Papers of Wilfred Trotter.* Oxford University Press, London. Permission to quote kindly granted by Oxford University Press, London.
5. Max Planck (1933). *Where is Science Going?* Trans. by James Murphy. George Allen & Unwin Ltd. Permission to quote kindly granted by George Allen & Unwin Ltd., London.
6. Albert Einstein (1933). Preface in *Where is Science Going?* by Max Planck. Trans. by James Murphy. George Allen & Unwin Ltd. Permission to quote kindly granted by George Allen & Unwin Ltd., London.
7. Francis Darwin (1888). *Life and Letters of Charles Darwin.* John Murray, London.
8. Theobald Smith (1929). *Am. J. Med. Sci.* 178, 740.
9. W. W. C. Topley and G. S. Wilson (1929). *The Principles of Bacteriology and Immunity.* Edward Arnold & Co., London.
10. F. M. R. Walshe (1944). "Some general considerations on higher or post-graduate medical studies." *Brit. Med. J.* Sept. 2nd, p. 297.
11. Hans Zinsser (1940). *As I Remember Him.* Macmillan & Co., Ltd., London; Little, Brown & Co., Boston; and the Atlantic Monthly Press. Permission to quote kindly granted by the publishers.
12. H. Florey (1946). *Brit. Med. Bull.* 4, 248.
13. J. T. Peters (1940). *Act. Med. Scand.* 126, 60.

APPLICATIONS

1. Read the preceding paper, noting how the author sets forth a series of closely reasoned points on the rationale of research. An

excellent way to master the content of such a paper is to prepare a paragraph outline of it. Do so now.

2. Working from your paragraph outline, prepare a corresponding topic outline.

3. Expand your topic outline to a full sentence outline, and write a thesis statement for it.

4. In how many paragraphs in "Reason" did you find a topic sentence as the first sentence of the paragraph? In how many paragraphs was a topic sentence implied? What generalizations can you draw from these observations?

5. In *Thinking Straight* Monroe C. Beardsley discusses the principles of reasoning for readers and writers. You can buy a paperback edition (Englewood Cliffs, N.J.: Prentice-Hall, 3rd ed., 1966) or borrow it from the library. Look it over, and then write a paper in which you compare and contrast Beardsley's point of view with the principles of logic for research workers as seen by Beveridge.

5 | What's the Idea?

The basic unit of organization is the paragraph. The basic function of the paragraph is to present an *idea*. Paragraphs can be looked at from two angles: their qualities and their parts. The qualities a paragraph must have are unity, coherence, and emphasis: each paragraph should be concerned with one, and *only one* idea; the parts of each paragraph should hang together; and each paragraph should stress what is important and soft-pedal what is not.

The parts of a paragraph, of course, are its sentences. The topic sentence summarizes the idea of the paragraph: it introduces the subject, and it states the attitude of the writer toward that subject. All other sentences in the paragraph *must* support the topic sentence.

Paragraph Length

With these points in mind, we may consider how long a paragraph should be. If you have been conditioned to thinking of paragraphs as Procrustean beds—which ideas must be stretched or lopped to fit—please put it out of your mind. A paragraph is simply a structural convenience for the reader, and it can be of any length within reason.

If the reader is in the mood for spot news, he will find the typical one-sentence paragraph of the newspaper column quite adequate. For example:

BERKELEY—A team of University of California scientists and a tiny beetle which grows its own space suit have given men a closer look at life in a microcosm than has ever before been possible.

The scientists have produced startling photographs of tissue, both living and dead, with a new device called the scanning electron microscope.

Their photograph of the head of a flour beetle is the first time living tissue has ever been photographed with such a device.

It has never been possible until now to photograph living specimens with an electron microscope because the instrument requires a vacuum and a heavy dose of radiation to operate.

Either one of these conditions would instantly kill living specimens. . . .[1]

Note how out-of-place this looks on a book page. Yet in a news column, it looks fine, as you can check by glancing at the nearest paper.

If the reader wants the kind of report that gives greater detail and more background information, he may turn to *Reader's Digest,* for example, and feel at ease with an average paragraph of three sentences or so. Like this:

When a volcano explodes almost anywhere on earth, the people in trouble tend to think of one man—a big, redheaded Belgian named

[1] Jim Hazelwood, "A Beetle Seen REALLY Close," *Oakland* (California) *Tribune,* December 2, 1966.

Haroun Tazieff. Often within minutes of the first rumble, a telegram is on its way to him, perhaps from Chile, the Philippines, Indonesia, Whatever the point of origin, the wording is essentially the same: VOLCANO ERUPTING STOP GREAT DANGER STOP POPULATION TERRIFIED STOP COME PLEASE.

Coming, wires Tazieff. And a few hours later he is making his way up a mountain, watching the parabolas of fire, timing the outbursts, getting ready to go deep into the crater, if necessary, to keep what he calls his "date with the devil."

Although others practice the trade of volcanology, Tazieff is the only one who goes so far into the depths of the erupting monster to diagnose its violence at close hand. Down where he goes, temperatures rise to 150 degrees Fahrenheit. The ground trembles. Up from the seething heart come whistles and shrieks and roars, flame and poisonous gases; and smoking incandescent rocks tumble through the scorched air. That Tazieff is alive today is a mountain-size miracle, for the maw of a volcano is as close to hell as a living person can go. . . .[2]

The long paragraph style, clear and economical of statement, may be found in the British scientific writings of a few decades ago. For example, in the following selection, Sir William Bragg tells of the serendipitous result of Max von Laue's 1912 experiment that showed that X-rays are similar to light. Note, however, how the long paragraphs are occasionally set off by short ones.

Let us now consider how it is that Laue's experiment was more than a mere verification of a well-imagined hypothesis. How does it come to give us these new opportunities?

We accept the evidence of Laue's experiment as proving the existence of a regular train of waves in the beam of X-rays, or at least that light and X-rays are alike. The regularity of structure of a crystal is also proved, if indeed it needed any further demonstration. Let us think what is implied by this latter regularity, which we have always imagined and are now to find so useful. Clearly, there is some inherent property of atoms and molecules which causes them to associate into very regular structures if the circumstances allow. When, for example, a solution of copper sulphate is evaporating and the molecules begin to sort themselves out of the liquid and to associate in groups, in other words to crystallize out, the preciseness and constancy of the form

---

[2] George Kent, "Hottest Job on Earth," *Reader's Digest,* 90 (January, 1967), 184–185.

which the grouping assumes tell us clearly that the solidification is not a mere gathering of the molecules into a jumble heap. The faces of any crystal of copper sulphate make the same angles with each other as the corresponding faces of any other crystal of copper sulphate. It is true that the circumstances of growth may affect the relative rates at which the faces grow, but this only means that more molecules have been added in certain directions than in others. We can draw from these facts no other deduction than this, that there is in the structure a unit of pattern containing copper, sulphur, and oxygen atoms in the same proportions as that in which they occur in the molecule. Further, each unit must lie up against each neighbouring unit in precise fashion; the relative orientation of the two and their relative distance apart being the same throughout the structure. The particular form of the crystal is a direct consequence of the particular structure of the unit. It is not possible, however, to deduce the latter from the former, or it would have been done long ago. But, now that the X-rays have come to our help, we obtain the power of looking past the outer appearance into the internal arrangement. The immense variety in the forms of various crystals, and the ease with which by precise measurements they can be distinguished from one another, are evidence of equal variety in the arrangement of the atoms and molecules in the unit and of equally precise distinctions. The structure of the single unit determines the properties of the solid substance. In many investigations of the behaviour of liquids and gases, in which the component molecules are not tied tightly together, the molecular form is of little consequence and it is sufficient to assume that it is spherical. But we cannot make this rough approximation when the molecules are associated into a solid crystal: for we should then blot out all those details which give each crystal its special characteristics. The chemical analysis of, for example, a piece of Iceland spar, calcium carbonate, begins with its solution in the appropriate reagents. The ties that make the solid are broken at the outset, and all that is found from the analysis are the relative numbers of atoms of calcium, carbon and oxygen. It is as if we knocked down a house and counted the number of bricks, planks, panes of glass, and so on: in doing which we lose count, of course, of those associations which made the conglomeration into a house.

We must bear in mind also that there is something even more important than the solid itself, namely the boundary between solid and liquid or gas. It is here that a vast number of changes continuously take place which are essential to the processes of Nature, animate and inanimate. At the surface the free disorder of the liquid comes into contact with the solid and its constrained regularity. The two phases meet, interchange existences, and exert mutual influences just as land and sea mutually encroach and affect each other. That is why the study of surface actions, of catalysis, and of colloidal phenomena are of such intense interest and importance. Now this surface action is greatly influenced by the orientation of the molecules of the solid; one face of a crystal for example has not the same properties as another. We cannot expect to understand the behaviour of the surface unless we know what is at the back of it in the solid, and whether the regularity of the solid is continued to the surface absolutely or is modified as it approaches the open, and how the molecule presents itself to the liquid or gas outside, and what are the special properties of the proportions so presented.

We have been making some use of the word molecule, which naturally stands for a certain combination of atoms known to us mainly from experiments with liquids and gases. As a matter of fact we have no right to do so; for it does not follow that, because a certain number of atoms take up a special arrangement when their company is free and independent, they necessarily retain the same arrangement when built with others into a structure. Our only justification is that we can actually recognize the molecule in the crystal in a very large number of cases. The recognition is not always clear, however, and we even find some cases in which there is such a regrouping of the atoms that a new molecule may be said to have been formed. There is always regularity in the arrangement within the crystal; but it is not strictly correct to say that it is an arrangement of the molecules unless the chemist will allow that his molecules can be altered: the change may be negligible in most cases but sometimes it is certainly considerable. If the alteration were so great that the chemical molecule was quite broken up and its atoms redistributed, then our new field of enquiry would not be less in any way than we now find it, because it would still include all the connexions between the properties of the solid and the atoms of which the solid is built; but we should lose a most interesting and useful connexion with the great results of chemistry. We may consider ourselves fortunate because the connexion is actually a strong one.

If it is not necessarily an arrangement of molecules, then, we must ask, what is it that is arranged?

We recognize at once that there must be some unit of pattern in the crystal; there must be an innumerable number of points such that if an observer, capable of taking up a position within the crystal and of noting the details of his surroundings, could be translated from any one of these points to any other, he would find no change in the outlook in any given direction in space. This supposes, of course, that the crystal extends to an infinite distance in all directions; but once the crystal is defined in this way we can suppose a finite crystal to be carved out of the infinite and to retain at the same time its structure, except perhaps in the neighborhood of the surface. This is the fundamental characteristic of the crystalline arrangement; that which is in the first line responsible for the observed X-ray effects—we shall presently see how—and which is always the first object of measurement.[3]

From the foregoing examples it will be clear that the answer to questions about optimum paragraph length is something like Abraham Lincoln's answer to how long a man's legs should be: "Long enough to reach the ground." Nevertheless, it is possible to suggest something approaching a norm. In technical writing, an average paragraph length of about five sentences will not be far from the mark. Note, though, that we are speaking of an *average*. Around such an average, effective paragraphs may consist of one sentence or two dozen.

In Sir William Bragg's discussion of crystal analysis, the lengths of the six paragraphs quoted are: 2, 19, 7, 7, 1, and 3 sentences. The average of these is 6.5, which is probably representative of the scientific writing of Bragg's day. A contemporary physicist would probably break the nineteen-sentence paragraph into two or three sub-paragraphs, to yield an average of five sentences or less. But even so, he would do well to approach Bragg's clarity of style and aptness of figure. In any case, the variety of paragraph length is worth noting—and well worth emulating. For occasional emphasis, the one-sentence paragraph is an especially effective device.

Paragraph Form

Subject to variations about a norm length, paragraphs may be developed in a variety of ways: by accumulating specific details, by comparing and contrasting elements, by showing a cause-and-

[3] William Bragg, *An Introduction to Crystal Analysis* (London: Bell, 1928), pp. 4–7. Used by permission.

effect relationship, by describing steps in a process, by extending a definition, by restating ideas previously expressed, or by presenting *a logical sequence of ideas*. Particularly important is a consideration of the *logical forms* paragraphs may take, and the most effective deployment of these forms throughout the composition.

THREE LOGICAL PARAGRAPH FORMS

In developing paragraphs following *a logical sequence of ideas,* three methods are especially useful. We may progress from the general to the particular, from the particular to the general, or by a combination of the two. Progression from the general to the particular gives a *deductive* paragraph; conversely, progression from the particular to the general gives an *inductive* paragraph.

To illustrate: A paragraph about Einstein's mass-energy relation might start with a statement concerning the equation $E = mc^2$, then take up specific details concerning Hiroshima, fusion reactions, and the submarine *Nautilus*. This would be a deductive paragraph. On the other hand, a paragraph might start with a recital of details about animals in the Galapagos, in Tierra del Fuego, and in the Andes and conclude with a brief summary of Darwin's theory of evolution. This would be an inductive paragraph.

You will see at once that these deductive and inductive orders of presentation correspond to the principles of reasoning that W. I. B. Beveridge discusses in relation to research (Chapter 4).

A graphical analogy will help to visualize the concept. A deductive paragraph can be likened to a cone resting on its base, with a topic sentence at its tip and a series of details (d_1, d_2, d_3, etc.) extending toward the base (see Figure 5.1). Turn such a cone upside down, and an inductive paragraph results (see Figure 5.2).

Of course, the cones may be arranged either base-to-base or tip-to-tip within a single indented paragraph, and if this is done, the result will be a *deductive-inductive* paragraph in the first case, or an *inductive-deductive* paragraph in the second case.

The *inductive-deductive* paragraph opens with details, states a topic sentence somewhere near the middle, and develops further details at the close. Or, it may even be limited to details, leaving

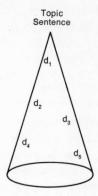

Figure 5.1. Deductive paragraph.

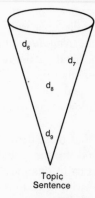

Figure 5.2. Inductive paragraph.

the reader to infer a topic sentence. The inductive-deductive paragraph can be very engaging when used in the informal or personal essay, but it tends to create a diffuse impression and thus has little place in technical writing.

In sharp contrast, the *deductive-inductive* paragraph is particularly effective for complex and closely reasoned presentations. It opens immediately on the matter at hand, develops the particulars that flow from it, and concludes by tying a firm knot at the end. True, a long series of deductive-inductive paragraphs may seem somewhat monotonous and mechanical, but the business of technical writing, after all, is to be clear—not to entertain. Thus, the deductive-inductive paragraph may be said to be the work horse of technical writing.

THE OVERALL PATTERN

Each of these logical paragraph forms is best suited for use at a particular point in the overall pattern. What is this pattern? The late Walter S. Campbell summed it up this way:

Every well-written piece has an over-all pattern which, as Aristotle tells us, must have a Beginning, a Middle, and an End. Each of these three portions of the over-all pattern should have a certain quality and arouse a certain kind of interest. Each also has its own specific problems.

1. The Beginning should be *clear* and should arouse *curiosity* in the reader.

2. The Middle should be *coherent* and should arouse *suspense* in the reader.

3. The End must be *brief* and inspire the reader with *satisfaction.*

If the Beginning is not clear, the reader will be puzzled, since he is turning from other thoughts and other matters to what you have to say, and unless you arouse curiosity in him at the start he will never follow through and read the rest of your piece.

The Middle must be coherent so that each item in it follows from and leads to another. Otherwise there can be no continuity and no suspense.

The End must be brief, because by the time the reader reaches the beginning of the End he already foresees it.[4]

This fine summary immediately suggests the logical forms of the paragraphs most suitable for the beginning, the middle, and the end.

THE BEGINNING

First, the reader's attention must be gained. Your opening sentence should therefore bridge the gap between his thought of

4 Walter S. Campbell, *Writing: Advice and Devices* (Garden City, N.Y.: Doubleday, 1950), p. 27. If at first glance this analysis impresses you as more applicable to fiction than to technical presentation, please turn back to "What Management Looks for in Technical Reports" and consider that in the light of the analysis.

the moment and what you need to tell him. It is sound to lead off with what Sheridan Baker calls an "innocuous and peaceable proposition . . . to which all readers would agree without rise in blood pressure."[5] Second, your beginning should arouse curiosity, and an effective device for this is the capsule preview. The thesis statement of the report will serve this purpose well and is most effectively placed at the end of the opening paragraph.

THE MIDDLE

The middle must be coherent. Coherence is not so much a matter of paragraph form per se as it is the alignment of forms from paragraph to paragraph. A continuous series of inductive paragraphs will give the reader a bumpy ride; so will a continuous series of deductive paragraphs. To return to the analogy of the cones, your best paragraph arrangement is tip-to-tip and base-to-base, taking care to avoid the diffuse inductive-deductive paragraph by not starting a paragraph at any point where bases meet (Figure 5.3).

THE END

From what we have already seen, it will be obvious that to be as brief as possible the closing paragraph should be inductive in form. Often it consists of restatement: first, of a few of the more striking details dealt with throughout the piece, and finally, of the main theme.

DESIGN OF THE OPENING PARAGRAPH

The opening paragraph of every report you write will carry the heaviest load, and you should give it your best effort. Writing effective opening paragraphs will be easier if you keep in mind the following design pattern.

First sentence: The topic sentence of the paragraph.
Middle sentences: These should follow from the topic sentence and lead logically to the final sentence.

[5] Sheridan Baker, *The Complete Stylist* (New York: Crowell, 1966), p. 62.

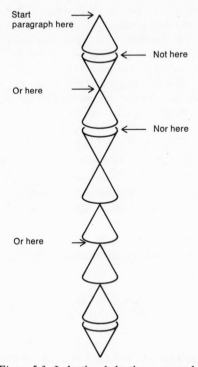

Figure 5.3. Inductive-deductive paragraph.

Last sentence: The thesis statement of the whole report (the same thesis statement as discussed on p. 68), or some suitable paraphrase of it.

An example of an excellent opening paragraph designed along these lines is the following.[6]

When primitive man succeeded in controlling fire for his warmth, food, and protection, he achieved the first milestone in man's continued quest for greater control over his environment. From the earliest dawn of civilization to the present, the advances in man's comfort, and often his knowledge, have been closely linked to his successes in harness-

[6] This is the opening paragraph of L. Talbot's "Energy Sources and Energy Conversion," which follows this chapter.

ing new sources of energy for his desired uses. The domestication of beasts of burden multiplied manyfold man's muscle power and made possible construction, farming, and transportation on a larger scale than he could achieve unaided. When he learned the art of constructing and navigating sailing vessels powered by the kinetic energy of the wind (and often aided by the broad back of the oarsman), he began his first serious explorations of the globe and his first ventures into commerce and intercourse between nations.

DESIGN OF PARAGRAPHS OF THE MIDDLE

You will recall that a particularly effective paragraph form for the middle of a report is the deductive-inductive. As an illustration of this, consider the following paragraph from the central section of "Energy Sources and Energy Conversion." Notice how the paragraph opens with a sharp topic sentence, proceeds from this to develop specific supporting details, and closes with a second topic sentence that refers back to the opening sentence by repeating a key term.

Our energy balance is very much like a bank account. When this planet was created, probably of material cast off from the sun, the earth received its fission-fuel inheritance. Much later, the sun added to our inheritance the fossil fuels. We are living on this inheritance today. But we also receive a steady "income," at a rate of about 120 watts per square foot or about 50 Q per year in the continental United States, from the sunlight which falls on the earth. Among other things, this income evaporates and elevates the water which is the source of our hydroelectric power, produces the wind which drives our sailboats and windmills, and provides the energy for the food we eat and the vegetation which some day may be transformed into new fossil fuels. Our daily income is in fact much greater than all our energy needs. But since we have not yet discovered how to manage our bank account prudently and live within our income, we must continue to dip into our inheritance.

DESIGN OF THE CLOSING PARAGRAPH

The most effective form for the closing paragraph is the inductive. The closing paragraph of "Energy Sources and Energy Conversion" follows. While the particulars here cited are indeed broad, they are surely details as compared to the concluding thesis statement.

The space program being pursued by the United States today affords us a good preview of the possible shape of things to come in power systems engineering. With the exception of thermonuclear power, all the energy-conversion devices we have discussed here, and many others that we have not had space to mention, are under active study and development in the search for power sources to meet the special needs of space exploration. For this reason, though his goals are in the sky, the space engineer's most significant victories may in the end be celebrated here on earth.

SUMMARY ON PARAGRAPH FORM

So far in this chapter we have considered matters of paragraph length and paragraph form. Sometimes the presentation has been rather arbitrary, and you may have thought that writing to such norms and forms could lead only to mechanical results—like copy churned from a computer. And you would be right. No writer—absorbed as he should be with his subject—has time to say consciously, "I shall now write a deductive-inductive paragraph." Nevertheless a subconscious appreciation of the strength of that form will stand him in good stead as he fills up his page. More important, a conscious application of the principles of paragraph form is an invaluable aid during revision, that *sine qua non* of the writing process, in which the writer turns from composition to criticism—the more severe the better—of his own work.

Paragraph Content

It is now time to turn to matters of paragraph content. We said earlier that paragraphs may be developed in the following ways:

- By accumulation of specific details
- By means of comparison and contrast
- By showing a cause-and-effect relationship
- By describing steps in a process
- By extending a definition
- By restating ideas previously expressed
- By a logical sequence of ideas

The latter we have just discussed at some length. Most of the others involve methods that you will use naturally as you find need for them, and it would serve no purpose to discuss them in detail. *Definition,* however, is so important in technical writing that we shall give an extended example of it.

DEFINITION

It is a rare technical report that does not use some definition. This may amount to no more than a simple stipulative definition such as: "For the purposes of this report 'highball' will mean 'a railroad signal for a train to proceed at full speed,' not 'a drink of spiritous liquor mixed with water or more often a carbonated beverage (as seltzer or ginger ale) and served in a tall glass usu. with ice.' "[7]

Some kinds of reports may require the use of many highly specialized terms. In such reports it is common to provide a separate section of "Definitions of Terms"; for convenience, this section is often printed on a fold-out sheet so that the definitions may be laid out beside the text.

Finally, certain kinds of reports consist almost entirely of definition. In these, the writer is usually concerned with answering one of two questions: "What does it *mean*?" or "What *is* it?"

For example, J. B. S. Haldane took more than 800 words to discuss what the word *hard* means and ended with the implication that he had barely scratched the surface.[8] In answer to the question "What *is* it?" Archibald A. Hill wrote a book chapter. Answering the question "What Is Language?" Hill provides a rewarding model for studying the variety of methods that a skilled writer may use in defining. It is offered in full in Appendix B. For the present, a bird's-eye view will suffice. The first paragraph follows, then outline topics of the succeeding paragraphs, and finally the closing paragraph.

The subject of linguistics presents an initial difficulty because the word which designates it is unfamiliar. The word can easily be defined as the

---

[7] *Webster's Third New International Dictionary, Unabridged* (Springfield, Mass.: Merriam, 1964).

[8] J. B. S. Haldane, *A Banned Broadcast and Other Essays* (London: Chatto & Windus, 1946), pp. 130–132.

scientific analysis of language, but it is doubtful if such a definition is meaningful to anyone who lacks familiarity with this kind of analytic activity. It is far better to begin by defining language, since language is closer to the reader's experience. Yet even the definition of language presents unsuspected difficulties and needs preliminary discussion before it is attempted directly.

- A productive definition of language will be attempted in what follows.
- Literate people are apt to think of writing as the real center of language.
- But speech is more basic and much older than writing.
- Linguists assume that language is a set of sounds.
- Description of language should begin with sounds, not with meanings.
- Five defining characteristics set off language from other symbolic behavior.
- First, language is a set of sounds.
- Second, the connection between sounds and objects is arbitrary and unpredictable.
- The most important statement about language is that it is social.
- Tones of voice and gestures accompanying speech are also largely arbitrary and socially learned.
- Third, language is synthetic.
- Every sentence is a frame, and a large group of other words can be substituted for any word in that frame.
- The entities of language are grouped into classes that are simpler than the varieties of objects in the world.
- The fourth defining characteristic of language is that it is a set of symbols different from those of other forms of communication.
- A given language entity can substitute for actual stimulus and actual response; men can discuss things they have never seen.
- A man in a cold room may make the direct response of closing the window.
- Or he may substitute a request to a friend to close the window.
- The last defining characteristic of language is that it is complete.
- This does not mean that every language has a word for everything. It does mean that the speakers of any language can coin whatever words they need.
- Thus, language may be defined as the primary and most highly elaborated form of human symbolic activity. In other words, every language is a model of a culture and its adjustment to the world.
- The study of language is important because it is the study most likely to throw light on the humanness of human nature.

- This study should lead to increased knowledge of society, better understanding of literature, and better language teaching.
- A student trained in language will have a sharper eye for pitfalls in communication.

By now, I hope that some meaning has been given to the definition of linguistics as the scientific study of language. Linguistics has for its goal the understanding of language, and it is secure in the belief that such understanding will increase human knowledge. It strives to present a picture of language as complete as possible, as consistent as possible, and as simple as possible, again secure in the belief that if these conditions are fulfilled it will be as truly and revealingly a science as is chemistry or astronomy. . . . The first stages of investigation and statement may seem to be disturbing and even to introduce confusion where none existed before, but as the design of language and its analysis unfold, clarity emerges, and with it the security of understanding.[9]

Paragraph Coherence

However adequate the individual paragraphs of a piece of writing may be as to length, form, and content, the reader will not turn the page unless the writing has continuity. Call it *flow,* or *forward drive* if you wish. Such flow is achieved in two ways: first, through logical ordering of the paragraphs, which is a problem of organization; and second, through the use of transitional devices, which link the paragraphs together. Walter S. Campbell has likened a good transition to a bridge, which *"must* be level, and *alike at both ends."*

Did you ever watch an elephant cross a bridge? How warily he tests every plank! Gingerly he thrusts his weight upon the yielding timbers. Keep that image before your mind's eye, for it is a portrait of your reader. He does not like bridges; he would rather not cross. You practically have to carry him over, by persuading him that what is on the other side is *just the same,* just as solid, as the ground on which he stands and hesitates.[10]

[9] Archibald A. Hill, *Introduction to Linguistic Structures* (New York: Harcourt, Brace & World, 1958), pp. 1–12.
[10] Walter S. Campbell, *Writing Non-Fiction* (Boston: The Writer, 1949), p. 78.

The writer has a wide choice in the transitional devices he may use. The more important ones of these are listed below for your ready reference.

- Repeating an important word in the last sentence of one paragraph in the first sentence of the next
- Using a synonym instead of repeating the word
- Rephrasing the idea of the last sentence of a paragraph in the first sentence of the next
- Using transitions from place to place, such as *to the right of the voltmeter, behind the field coil, inside the thermal shield,* and so on
- Using markers of time, such as *before, after, in the meantime,* and so on
- Using stepping stones like *however, nevertheless, yet, on the other hand, then, too, then too, also, in spite of, still, in the first place, second, next,* and so on.

Turn now to "Energy Sources and Energy Conversion," which follows. You will quickly sense a style distinguished for its clarity and easy flow. This, of course, is the result of many factors besides skillful paragraph development. For the present, however, you are asked to study the selection principally from the standpoints of paragraph form, paragraph content, logic of paragraph sequence, and paragraph coherence.

Energy Sources
and Energy Conversion

L. Talbot

Larry Talbot was born in New York City and received his B.S., M.S., and Ph.D. degrees from the University of Michigan, the last degree in engineering mechanics with specialization in fluid dynamics. He served as instructor and research assistant in the Aero Research Center at the University of Michigan. In 1951 he joined the University of California, and is currently professor of aeronautical sciences in the Department of Mechanical Engineering at Berkeley. He has made many research contributions on shock wave structures, free-molecule and slip flow, viscous-interaction phenomena, low-density plasma jets, and other aspects of fluid dynamics. His work in energy conversion has been in the field of magnetohydrodynamics.

Dr. Talbot has acted as consultant on rarefied gas dynamics for the Sandia Corporation, the Atomic Energy Commission, the Ingersol-Rand Company, the General Electric Missiles and Space Vehicles Department, the Litton Industries, and the Bendix Aviation Corporation, as well as for other companies and government agencies. His many guest lectures include a series sponsored by NATO in England, France, Holland, Belgium, and Germany.

The Energy Revolution

When primitive man succeeded in controlling fire for his warmth, food, and protection, he achieved the first milestone in man's continued quest for greater control over his environment. From the earliest dawn of civilization to the present, the advances in man's comfort, and often his knowledge, have been closely linked to his successes in harnessing new sources of energy for his desired uses. The domestication of beasts of burden multiplied manyfold man's muscle power and made possible construction, farming, and transportation on a larger scale than he could achieve unaided. When he learned the art of constructing and navigating sailing vessels powered by the kinetic energy of the wind (and often aided by the broad back of the oarsman), he began his first serious explorations of the globe and his first ventures into commerce and intercourse between nations.

Without doubt the most important milestone in the history of man's utilization of energy sources was the development in the late eighteenth century of a practical device which for the first time made possible the use of the chemical energy of wood and coal to drive all kinds of industrial machines. This device was the steam engine. Although the idea of using a fluid to absorb heat and by subsequent expansion to do work (the principle of all heat engines) was known to Hero of Alexandria, it was not until after James Watt's innovations between 1760 and 1790 that the steam engine became an efficient heat engine.

With the steam engine came the *industrial revolution* and, as we shall see, the beginning of what might be termed the *energy revolution,* a concerted and ever broadening attack on the energy resources of the planet. In the period between 1830 and 1860, reaction and impulse turbines for extracting the potential energy of water stored at high heads were developed. These developments were followed closely by the achievements of Otto, Daimler, and Diesel between 1874 and 1895, which led to practical internal combustion engines that could operate on liquid hydrocarbon fuels, such as oil, gasoline, and kerosene. At about the same time, Parsons developed the steam turbine, and not long after this, at about the beginning of the twentieth century, the first steam turbine-driven electric power generating plants went into operation.

We see about us today the fruits of the industrial and energy revolutions. Energy is being devoured in tremendous quantities by automobiles and airplanes, by more and better-heated homes and with multitudinous electrical appliances, and by vast manufacturing and processing industries. Not only has the per capita energy consumption risen steadily, but the population has climbed along with it. With more people and more energy demand per person, it is inevitable that we should ask: What are our energy resources? How long will they last? What new energy sources should we be investigating and exploiting?

These are not easy questions to answer. Even though exhaustive studies have been made, such as those listed in the Bibliography, one finds that the answers arrived at involve a great deal of guesswork and extrapolation, and are subject to considerable uncertainty. For this reason, and because of our limitations of space, we shall here discuss these questions in only very broad outline, and will restrict our discussion to the United States. However, since the United States is estimated to possess about 15 per cent of the total world reserve of fossil fuels (oil, coal, gas) and to account for about 37 per cent of the present total world power consumption, the figures we shall present are in a sense representative of the world situation.

Energy Consumption Now and in the Future

We will be talking about vast quantities of energy. A unit of energy which has been found convenient for such discussions is the Q which is defined as 10^{18} Btu. (Recall that the *British Thermal Unit,* or Btu, is defined as the heat necessary to raise by one degree Fahrenheit the temperature of one pound of water, and 10^{18} represents a billion billion, that is, 10 followed by 17 zeros.) To give a physical idea of the size of the Q, it represents the heat liberated by the combustion of 38 billion tons of bituminous coal. To give another example, if we had 400 million automobiles, each with a 100-horsepower engine, and ran them all at full throttle night and day for an entire year, we would consume an amount of gasoline equivalent to about one Q of energy.

A graph of the *accumulated total energy* consumed in the United States from 1800 to 1960, and extrapolated to A.D. 2000, is shown in Fig. 1. The United States passed the 1-Q total-consumption mark about 1940, and if the hypothetical extrapolation to the future is valid, we should hit the 10-Q mark a little after A.D. 2000.

The *annual* United States energy consumption in 1962 was

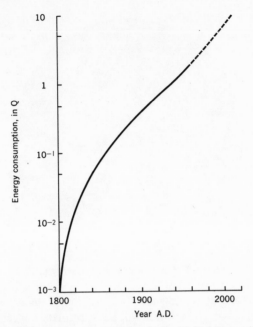

Figure 1. Cumulative energy consumption in the United States, in *Q*. (From Putnam's *Energy in the Future,* Copyright 1953, D. Van Nostrand Company, Inc., Princeton, N.J., Fig. 9–12.)

about 0.03 Q. Of this, roughly two-thirds, or 0.02 Q, was supplied by oil and natural gas, and the remaining third by coal. Water power and wood combustion accounted for roughly 5 per cent of the total, and surprisingly, wood was about five times as important as water power as an energy source.

The way the United States "energy pie" is presently cut up is of interest. This is shown in Fig. 2. One sees that the energy expended in electric power generation (mainly from steam plants operating on coal) is about 15 per cent of the total energy consumed. About 30 per cent goes for comfort heating of homes, office buildings, and factories. About 10 per cent goes for *process heating,* that is, heat expended in refining, manufacturing, etc. Approximately 20 per cent of the total is consumed by automobiles, and the remainder is accounted for by work-producing devices of various types, such as reciprocating- and jet-engine air-

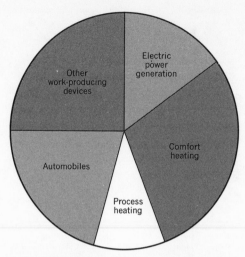

Figure 2. The United States "energy pie."

planes, tractors, diesel engines. The division of energy usage is of interest in its own right, but it will be of primary concern when we consider the possible new forms of energy which might become available, and what kinds of devices will be needed to tap these new energy sources.

Our Fossil Fuel Reserves

We have seen that oil, natural gas, and coal provide almost all the energy consumed in the United States, and that this consumption now is at an annual rate of about 0.03 Q. How much oil (we shall lump natural gas with oil) and how much coal do we have, and how long can they be expected to last at the rates we are expected to consume them in the coming years?

According to some geologists, there is more oil and coal in the earth than we shall ever need. But the amount that is economically recoverable at, say, no more than twice the present costs of mining and drilling is quite limited. Typical energy estimates for economically recoverable reserves are about 0.5 Q for oil-gas, and about 6.0 Q for coal. Thus, at our present rate of consumption, and assuming no importation, the United States oil reserves might last only about $0.5/0.02 = 25$ years, and our coal might last $6.0/0.01 = 600$ years. These estimates do not account for the steady trend of increased annual consumption shown in Fig. 1. If the 1960 figures on population growth and the consumption per capita are extrapolated to A.D. 2000, one finds that the annual fossil fuel consumption might rise to more than 0.1 Q per year and at this rate, the estimated present United States oil-gas reserves would last only 7½ years! Of course, we can produce oil and gasoline from coal, at roughly a yield of 1 Btu of liquid fuel for 2 Btu of coal, so we should really consider the combined coal and oil reserves. Thus, if we used coal alone to meet both our liquid and solid fuel needs, then at the present rate of consumption, our coal reserves might run out in about 120 years.

The numbers we have been talking about are very rough estimates based on assumptions, extrapolations, and pure guesses too numerous to mention. The estimated life expectancies of our fossil fuel reserves may be too small by as much as a factor of 10. But if the numbers are at all correct, they indicate that with our present pattern of energy consumption, we might face oil shortages within the next few decades, and perhaps coal shortages within the next few hundred years.

If we assume that this is true, what can we do about it? What are some of the possible short-range solutions to the problem? Are there any promising long-range ones? If we continue to increase our standard of living and continue to live "high on the energy hog," as it were, then answers for these problems will have to be found. Finding them may involve engineers and scientists in possibly the most significant and challenging research and development since the start of the industrial-energy revolution.

Increasing Our Efficiency of Energy Utilization

One of the first things one asks with regard to prolonging the life of our fossil fuel reserves is whether they can be utilized more efficiently. The prospects for significant gain here are not bright if the pattern of energy consumption continues essentially as it exists today. About 60 per cent of the energy we consume goes into the production of work by heat engines (internal-combustion engines, steam turbines, etc.). The efficiency of a heat machine, that is, the fraction of the fuel energy which we get out as useful work, is governed by a fundamental thermodynamic law, known as Carnot's theorem. It states that the maximum efficiency e_{max} of conversion of heat into work cannot exceed the value[1]

$$e_{max} = \frac{T_{max} - T_{min}}{T_{max}} \tag{1}$$

where T_{max} is the maximum temperature at which heat is added, and T_{min} is the lowest temperature at which heat is rejected. (Heat *must* be thrown away in a heat engine cycle, as for example, in the exhaust steam from a steam turbine or in the exhaust and cooling water of an automobile engine. It is an unfortunate but inescapable fact of thermodynamic life, known as the Second Law, that heat cannot be converted completely into work in any heat engine.) In practice, the efficiencies achieved fall far short of the maximum efficiencies given by Eq. (1). Typical values are around 25 per cent for optimum operation of an automobile engine, 35 per cent for a diesel engine, and 40 per cent for the most modern high-pressure (5,000 psi) steam-turbine power plant. Improvements in these heat engine efficiencies are possible but hard to achieve, since they invariably involve higher operating temperatures (higher T_{max}), which in turn mean better high-temperature materials. Process and comfort heating, which account for the remaining 40 per cent of our energy consumption, is more efficient, and efficiencies here can get up around 50 to 60 per cent. The overall average efficiency of energy conversion in the United States is estimated at about 30 per cent. Thus, unless we produce a substantial portion of our work requirements by devices other than heat engines, we cannot hope for dramatic improvements on the total overall efficiency of energy conversion. Nevertheless, with our huge energy consumption, one percentage point of increased efficiency can mean large dollar savings, so engineers today continue to work hard on ways of bettering heat engine performance.

---

[1] The temperatures in this formula are absolute temperatures, found by adding 460° to the Fahrenheit values. Thus 70°F = 530°R, where R stands for Rankine.

One modern approach to station power generation which seeks to increase thermal efficiency is the *magnetohydrodynamic* (MHD) *power generator*. Basically, an MHD generator operates on the same principle as a conventional electric generator. In the latter, when a conductor, usually copper, is passed through a magnetic field, an electric current is induced in it. In the MHD generator, a stream of ionized, electrically conducting gas replaces the copper conductor. The gas flows across a magnetic field, and the current induced is drawn out in an external circuit, as shown in Fig. 3. To make a gas a good electrical conductor, it must be heated to very high temperatures, in excess of 6000°F, even when the gas is "seeded" with small amounts of an easily ionized metal vapor such as potassium in order to enhance its conductivity. This heating could be accomplished through the combustion of coal, kerosene, or other fossil fuels. Only part of the power potential of the hot ionized gas can be obtained from the current induced by the magnetic field. The gas, still hot after passing through the magnetic field, can then be used to generate steam and produce additional electrical power by means of a conventional steam turbine-electric generator arrangement. The theoretical efficiency of MHD power generation is higher than that of conventional steam power because the use of an ionized gas permits a higher maximum temperature, and in the case of MHD generators, overall efficiencies approaching 56 per cent are hoped for.

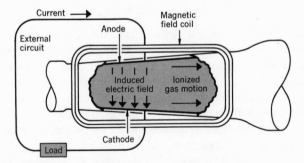

Figure 3. Direct-current magnetohydrodynamic generator. (Adapted from R. J. Rosa and A. Kantrowitz, "Magnetohydrodynamic Energy Conversion Technique," AVCO Research Report No. 86, April, 1959.)

The MHD generator is not yet a practical reality. The high temperatures involved, which from a thermodynamic point of view are necessary for high efficiency, pose many technical problems in electrode design and materials which are not yet solved. Very high magnetic fields are necessary, which appear to be obtainable on a large scale only by using superconducting coils cooled to near absolute zero temperature—a curious marriage of hot and cold which presents additional technical problems. Moreover, the MHD generator produces direct current, so that conversion to alternating current is necessary to integrate MHD power into existing electrical power systems.

Despite all these problems, hopes have been expressed that practical MHD generators will be operating within the next ten years. One line of current thinking is that they will be used as *topping plants,* combined with conventional steam-turbine power plants, to provide electric power at times of peak demand. From an economic point of view, it is estimated that the greater capital investment necessary for an MHD-generator plant would make MHD power, despite its higher efficiency of generation, cost about the same as power produced today in conventional steam plants in the United States. However, in countries where fuel costs are higher and capital costs lower, economic savings might be achieved by using MHD generators, provided the hoped-for performance of the MHD plant is realized.

Atomic Energy as a New Source of Energy

The first controlled nuclear fission chain reaction was achieved in Chicago in 1942. In the little more than twenty years since that historic event, the technology and science of fission reactors have advanced to the point at which today's private power companies are building multi-megawatt atomic power plants which they consider economically competitive with coal-fired plants.

Most of us are familiar to some extent with the basic ideas of the atomic power generator, as exemplified by the schematic diagram of Fig. 4. The nuclear fuel is usually some mixture of uranium 235 and uranium 238. (Natural uranium is a mixture of

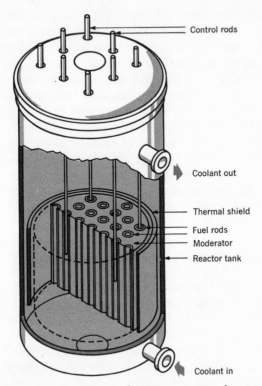

Figure 4. Schematic arrangement of a power reactor shows uranium fuel rods, moderator, thermal shielding, and reactor vessel. The coolant carries off heat developed by fissioning U²³⁵ atoms. Control rods hold reaction at a proper level by absorbing excess neutrons. (Adapted from Skrotzki and Vopat, *Power Station Engineering and Economy,* McGraw-Hill Book Company, 1960, Fig. 21-1.)

these two isotopes in the proportion 99.3 per cent U^{238} and 0.7 per cent U^{235}.) The U^{235} is capable of sustaining a chain reaction. When the nucleus of a U^{235} atom is penetrated by a neutron moderated to the proper energy, the nucleus, which is in a precarious state of equilibrium, may fly apart into smaller fragments which are lower-atomic-weight elements and elementary particles. In the process of this fission, additional neutrons are released (between one and two per fission) which are then available for fissioning other U^{235} atoms. The key to the energy release is Einstein's famous law of the equivalence between mass and energy, $E = mc^2$, where m is the mass and c the speed of light. When a uranium atom fissions, the fragments turn out to have less total mass than the original atom (the whole, in terms of mass, is greater than the sum of its parts). The mass difference is accounted for by the energy released in fission in the form of radiation and kinetic energy of the fission fragments. Ultimately, much of the liberated energy ends up as heat. In an ordinary chemical reaction such as the burning of coal, the energy released corresponds to a mass loss so small, about one part in 40 billion, that it is undetectable. But when a uranium atom fissions, the mass loss is much greater, so much so that the fission of 1 pound of uranium releases energy equivalent to the combustion of nearly 1,500 tons of coal.

The heat produced in the fission process is transferred within the reactor to a circulating liquid coolant, often a liquid metal such as sodium. Outside the reactor, the coolant passes through a heat exchanger, and in so doing boils water to produce steam. The steam thus generated goes to a turbine to produce electrical power. In effect, then, the nuclear fission reactor operates in much the same way as a steam power plant, except that the heat is supplied by energy released in nuclear fission rather than in the combustion of coal.

The main advantage of the nuclear reactor is that a single charge of nuclear fuel may generate power for several years before it has to be replaced. Although U^{235} is not plentiful in nature, it is a fortunate circumstance that the relatively abundant U^{238} can be converted within a reactor through neutron capture to a chain-reacting element, plutonium 239. This process is known as *breeding*. Similarly, natural thorium can be bred into chain-reacting U^{233}. It has been estimated that the world supply of natural uranium and thorium is equivalent in energy to more than *twenty* times the world's coal and oil, so it is conceivable that nuclear reactors may gradually replace coal-fired plants as coal becomes more uneconomical to mine. Today, despite the much greater first costs of a nuclear plant and the problems of radiation shielding and radioactive waste disposal, power produced over a period of years by nuclear fission may become cheaper than coal power in many locations where coal transportation expenses are high.

The practicality of electric power generation by atomic fission in large power stations is firmly established. But electric power generation accounts for only about 15 per cent of our energy demand. What about the other 85 per cent? Assuming that our fossil fuel reserves are as limited as some current estimates indicate, will we be able to fill the breach with atomic energy when coal and oil supplies begin to dwindle? Can we use nuclear reactors to heat our homes, run our automobiles, trucks, and airplanes, and provide heat for refining and manufacturing? To some of these questions, such as home heating by central-station reactor-generated electricity, the answer is undoubtedly yes, but to others the answer is clearly negative.

Nuclear reactors, unless adequately shielded, emanate deadly radiation. Shielding is bulky and heavy, and therefore reactors are practical only where large size and weight can be tolerated. A reactor is practical in a submarine or ocean vessel, but not in a small motor launch or airplane or automobile. In addition to the shielding problems, there are other hazards involved in the operation of nuclear reactors which make unlikely their safe use by the general public. As far as private transportation is concerned, the thought of thousands of nuclear-reactor-powered automobiles being demolished on the highways each year, strewing radioactive materials about, is too horrifying for even the most sanguine of visionaries to contemplate. Even apart from the hazards, the nuclear reactor is basically not an ideal power device for automobiles because it is suited more for steady power demand than for the intermittent on-off service required from an automobile. For the same reason, nuclear reactors are unsuited for use in commercial and private airplanes, although arguments have been made for the military utility of a nuclear-powered airplane which could stay aloft for indefinite periods of time without refueling.

Atomic Batteries and Thermoelectric Devices

If, as some predict, nuclear reactor power stations begin to supplant coal-fired ones, then we shall be faced with an immense problem of fission-product disposal. Several disposal techniques are currently in use. One method is to store the wastes underground for a long enough time to allow the radioactivity to decay. In another method, fission products are sealed in containers which are then encased in concrete blocks and sunk in deep parts of the ocean. It would be nice if a large-scale use could be found for fission products, which would both provide additional payoff for the nuclear reactor and lessen the disposal problem. Atomic batteries conceivably could accomplish this end.

Many types of atomic batteries which convert radiation and heat energy into electrical energy are being investigated in laboratories today. We shall mention only one, the thermocouple battery, which is probably the simplest to understand.

When two dissimilar strips of metal are joined together at both ends to form a loop, and the two junctions, called *thermocouples,* are kept at different temperatures, a current flows in the loop. This is the *thermoelectric effect,* and represents a process which, from the power engineer's point of view, is highly desirable, namely, the direct conversion of heat into electricity without moving parts. At first glance it might appear that, with such direct conversion, the efficiency of thermoelectric power generation would not be limited by Carnot's theorem. But in fact heat is added at the hot junction and rejected at the cold junction of the thermocouple loop, and the theoretical thermoelectric generation efficiency is identical to that of a heat engine operating between the same temperature limits. In its simplest form, the atomic battery consists of a thermocouple circuit, with one junction heated by the energy liberated from a reactor-produced radioactive isotope, such as polonium 210. Connecting an external load to the battery terminals closes the circuit and permits current to flow.

Thermoelectric power sources are still in their infancy, and a tremendous amount of development work will be required if ever they are to assume a prominent role in energy generation. At present, these power generators run at much lower efficiencies than what is theoretically obtainable. Nevertheless, they have already been used with atomic heat sources in some satellites, and have been used with simple kerosene heat sources to power radios.

Possibly what will make the thermoelectric device practical will be an ingenious combination with some form of semiconductor current multiplier. Work in this direction is being pursued in many laboratories. Other thermionic devices, such as *plasma diodes* and certain semiconductors, which we do not have space to discuss here, are also being investigated today.

Fuel Cells

The direct conversion of chemical energy into electricity without the intermediate generation and flow of heat is very desirable, because one is then not limited by the restrictions on maximum efficiency imposed by the Carnot theorem. It is not surprising therefore, that a tremendous amount of effort is being expended on the development of devices which might achieve this end. Thus far, the most promising of these devices appears to be the *fuel cell*.

Basically, the fuel cell is a device in which the energy liberated by a chemical reaction appears not as heat, but instead appears immediately as an electric current flowing under an impressed voltage. In appearance, fuel cells have many features in common with conventional storage batteries, except for the important distinction that the fuels which undergo reaction in the fuel cell flow continuously through the cell.

Many different fuels have been used in fuel cells. In some cells the chemical reaction can be achieved at essentially room temperature, in others high temperatures are required. To illustrate the basic principles of operation, we will consider the low-temperature hydrogen-oxygen fuel cell in which these two gases react to produce an electric current and water.

A schematic diagram of a hydrogen-oxygen fuel cell is shown in Fig. 5. It consists of two porous electrodes, typically made of carbon impregnated with suitable catalysts, immersed in an electrolyte which might be a concentrated solution of sodium or potassium hydroxide. The hydrogen side is the negative side, and the oxygen the positive side. On the negative side, the hydrogen gas diffusing through the carbon electrode reacts at the electrode inside

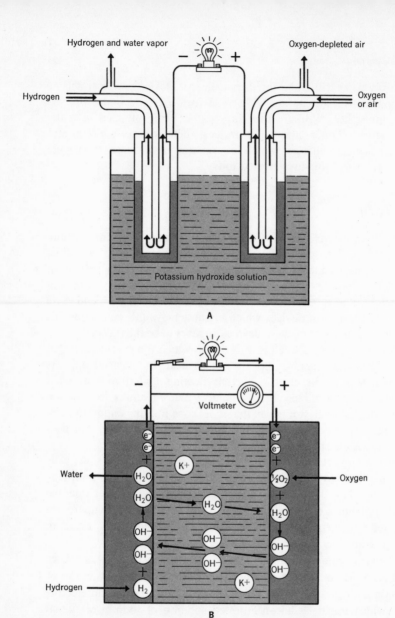

Figure 5. (A) A hydrogen-oxygen fuel cell consists of two porous carbon electrodes (dotted areas) and an electrolyte such as potassium hydroxide. Hydrogen enters one side, and oxygen the other. Both gases diffuse into the electrodes, reacting to form water. Liberated electrons flow through the circuit. (B) When the circuit is closed, the gases and electrolyte react to produce a flow of electrons. A catalyst embedded in the electrode dissociates hydrogen gas molecules into individual atoms, which combine with hydroxyl ions in the electrolyte to form water. The process yields electrons to the electrode. Electron and ion flow produces the desired current. (From Leonard G. Austin, "Fuel Cells," *Scientific American,* pp. 73, 74, October, 1959. Reprinted with permission. Copyright © 1959 by Scientific American, Inc. All rights reserved.)

surface with negative OH^- ions in the electrolyte to produce H_2O and free electrons e^-. The reaction is

$$H_2 + 2OH^- \longrightarrow 2H_2O + 2e^- \qquad (2)$$

The free electrons flow through the external circuit and constitute the electric output of the cell; the water produced goes into the electrolyte.

On the positive side of the cell, air or oxygen diffuses through the electrode. The electrons which arrive from the external circuit react with oxygen and with water in the electrolyte to produce OH^- hydroxyl ions. These ions then diffuse through the electrolyte to take part in the chemical reaction at the hydrogen side. The migration of the OH^- ions through the electrolyte provides the current which closes the circuit within the cell. The reaction at the oxygen side is

$$H_2O + \tfrac{1}{2}O_2 + 2e^- \longrightarrow 2OH^- \qquad (3)$$

The electrolyte and the catalysts in the electrodes promote the reactions but do not actually take part in them. However, the electrolyte becomes progressively more diluted by the water generated in the reaction.

Low-temperature and -pressure hydrogen-oxygen cells have the disadvantage of typically producing only about one kilowatt of power per cubic foot of volume, and hydrogen is an expensive fuel. This performance can be bettered by as much as six times by operating at high pressure and somewhat elevated temperature. The Bacon hydrogen-oxygen, nickel-electrode cell which operates at up to 250°C and 800 psi can produce as much as fifteen times the power per pound as a conventional lead-acid automobile battery. Efficiencies as high as 75 per cent have been obtained, much greater than the best heat engine. Like the conventional battery, the fuel cell is a low-voltage, direct-current device, delivering somewhat less than one volt per cell, so many must be connected in series to provide the voltage required for most direct-current machines.

Considerable effort is being directed today toward developing fuel cells which operate efficiently on cheap fuels, such as natural gas, gasoline, or coal. Operation with these fuels requires temperatures above 500°C, and presents additional problems not found in lower temperature cells. To date, performance of high-temperature fuel cells has been poor in comparison with the hydrogen-oxygen cell. Of course, the fuel economics of tomorrow may be quite the reverse of today; hydrogen produced by the electrolysis of water conceivably could one day be cheaper than hard-to-find oil and natural gas.

The proponents of fuel cells envision their eventual use in a variety of applications. Suggestions have been advanced for their installation in large nuclear power stations to provide electricity at times of peak demand. At times of low power demand, excess reactor power could be used for the electrolysis of water, thus providing the hydrogen necessary for the fuel cell operation at times of peak demand. As in the case of MHD power, the direct-current output of fuel cells would have to be converted to alternating current.

If a satisfactory high-output fuel cell or a high-output, rapidly rechargeable battery can be developed, we might very well see the return of the electric automobile. The electric automobile is in principle quite attractive for several reasons. Electric motors are simpler, quieter, and more efficient than internal-combustion engines. Moreover, they do not produce air pollutants. A demonstration that fuel cell-driven mobile transportation is at least within the realm of possibility was provided by the Allis-Chalmers Company with their experimental tractor powered by 1,008 hydrogen-oxygen fuel cells, shown in Fig. 6.

The prospects appear bright for the eventual widespread use of fuel cells. But much development and engineering will be required. As one researcher has put it, "Fuel-cell development is not a field for the faint-hearted."

Energy From the Sun

Our energy balance is very much like a bank account. When this planet was created, probably of material cast off from the sun, the earth received its fission-fuel inheritance. Much later, the sun added to our inheritance the fossil fuels. We are living on this inheritance today. But we also receive a steady "income," at a rate

Figure 6. An experimental farm tractor developed by Allis-Chalmers, powered by 1,008 fuel cells. (From Eric Eltham, "The Fuel Cell: Promise or Threat to the Petroleum Industry," *World Petroleum,* November, 1961.)

of about 120 watts per square foot or about 50 Q per year in the continental United States, from the sunlight which falls on the earth. Among other things, this income evaporates and elevates the water which is the source of our hydroelectric power, produces the wind which drives our sailboats and windmills, and provides the energy for the food we eat and the vegetation which some day may be transformed into new fossil fuels. Our daily income is in fact much greater than all our energy needs. But since we have not yet discovered how to manage our bank account prudently and live within our income, we must continue to dip into our inheritance.

We have not yet succeeded in meeting our energy expenditures with current income because thus far all the methods we have for capturing large amounts of the sun's energy are woefully inefficient. As an example, we may consider the amount of energy that can be recovered by making use of the natural photosynthesis occurring in plants. As is well known to racing enthusiasts, alcohol is an acceptable motor fuel. It can be obtained by fermentation of many different plants, such as corn, potatoes, sugar beets, various grains, etc. About the largest yield is obtained from sugar beets, which produce at maximum about 300 gallons of alcohol per acre. This, unfortunately, is but a trifling amount when compared to our *daily* gasoline consumption of 170 million gallons. The best photosynthetic yields achieved to date apparently have been with a species of single-celled algae called *Chlorella*. In a pilot plant built in the early 1950's, it was found that these algae, when grown in water, absorbed and converted up to 2 per cent of the solar energy falling on them—a yield about twenty times better than the photosynthetic efficiency of sugar beets. Even so, an area about equal to the state of Indiana would be required to grow enough *Chlorella* for fermentation to satisfy our current motor fuel needs. Evidently, the prospect of supplying motor-fuel alcohol by photosynthesis is rather dim, in terms of what we know about it today. If *Chlorella* farming on a large scale were ever seriously considered, some differences of opinion would undoubtedly arise as to which state or states should be swamped by seas of algae for the good of the rest of the nation.

More promising are the possibilities that many of our future homes may be heated by solar energy, and that small devices will be powered by solar cell-generated electricity. Solar cells, which have already found widespread use in satellites and space vehicles, are now reaching efficiencies between 10 and 15 per cent, so that in bright sunlight they can produce well over 10 watts per square foot of irradiated area. With this kind of power output we are not going to be able to run automobiles, but, on the other hand, a 1,000-square-foot solar cell panel could easily provide enough battery-charging current to meet the electrical needs of a normal household, if the climatic conditions were reasonably favorable. A 1,000-square-foot panel could also provide the power necessary to boil roughly one pound of water every two minutes, which suggests that solar cells might ultimately be useful in certain arid areas to distill salt water. Of course, the figures cited show only the technical feasibilities of the various applications. Before any one of the proposed schemes could become a reality on more than a laboratory scale, much engineering development would have to be done, and what is most important, the scheme would have to be more economical than the available alternatives.

Probably, hydroelectric power generation will continue to be the most significant use of our daily income from the sun. At present in the United States, hydroelectricity accounts for roughly 20 per cent of the station power generated, or a little over one per cent of our total energy consumption. The trend, however, has actually been away from water power in recent years. In 1940, for example, 33 per cent of our electricity was hydrogenerated, and in 1920 the figure was 40 per cent. It has been estimated that if all the hydroelectric resources in the United States were actually developed, they might be able to supply about 5 per cent of our total energy needs. Clearly, hydroelectricity will not provide the solution to a fossil-fuel shortage. It will, however, continue to be an important power source in the United States, and even more so in certain other parts of the world. It is quite possible, for example, that the industrialization of the African continent may depend crucially on the development of its hydroelectric potential.

Thermonuclear Power

If we are unable to find ways to live on the sun's "income," perhaps we can here on earth mimic the sun's method for producing its tremendous energy output. Such is the goal of thermonuclear power, or as it has more dramatically been put, "taming the H-bomb."

The nuclear reaction which is responsible for the sun's energy and for the explosive energy release of the hydrogen bomb is the *fusion* or *thermonuclear* reaction. The fusion reaction is the opposite of the fission reaction referred to previously, because in the fusion reaction two light nuclei combine, or fuse, to form a heavier one. But the energy released by this process is governed by the same law as the fission reaction, Einstein's $E = mc^2$ equation. It seems that when two nuclei of certain of the lighter elements are fused, the result is a nucleus of less total mass than was contained in the two nuclei before fusion. As in the case of the fission reaction, the mass defect appears as liberated energy. Fusion reactions are more energetic than fission reactions; typically, more than ten times as much energy is liberated per fusion than per fission.

There are many possible energy-liberating fusion reactions. We shall discuss only one—the deuterium-deuterium (D-D) reaction —not only because it is one of the best understood but also because it is by far the most important for power generation. Deuterium is an isotope of hydrogen and differs from the latter in that the deuterium nucleus contains a neutron in addition to the proton of the normal hydrogen atom. The most abundant source of deuterium is natural water, in which this element is found in the form of deuterium oxide, D_2O, sometimes called "heavy water." About 3 out of every 20,000 water molecules in the ocean are D_2O molecules. Our supply of deuterium is therefore, for all practical purposes, limitless.

In a fission reactor, all that one has to do is to bring enough U^{235} together (the critical size) to prevent excessive leakage of neutrons, and the chain reaction "goes." The fissionable fuel does not have to be preheated, nor do any special temperature-insulation precautions have to be taken, because by carefully controlling the rate at which neutrons produce new fissions, almost any level of power generation can be maintained. The fusion reactor is another matter altogether. To fuse two deuterium nuclei together requires a tremendous kinetic energy of impact. The kinetic energy of gas particles increases with their temperature, and to produce fusion one must achieve the temperature which exists in the interior of the sun, over 100 million °C. In brief, the problem of the fusion reactor is to heat deuterium to this very high temperature, and to hold it together for a sufficiently long time to permit the fusion reaction to take place at a controlled rate. Somehow, also, the energy liberated in the fusion process must be harnessed as useful power. In a hydrogen bomb, fusion temperatures are produced by the explosion of fissionable material, and the fusion reaction is likewise an explosive liberation of energy. What is necessary is to change in some way the fusion "bang" to a "whimper" so to speak. In view of the differences between the fission and fusion processes, it is not surprising that, whereas the fission reactor preceded the atomic bomb, the H-bomb has not yet been "tamed."

How do you heat a gas to 100 million degrees? And even if you could get a gas that hot, what would you hold it in? Physicists and engineers working on thermonuclear power are today searching for the answers to these questions. Many different and novel devices have been built and tested, and more are on the way. All these devices, however, have one essential feature in common— the use of magnetic fields to confine the hot gas.

To understand the essential ideas of magnetic confinement, we must first understand what happens to any material when it is heated to the very high temperatures we are concerned with. At these temperatures, all matter becomes gaseous. More than that, it becomes completely ionized, in that the electrons surrounding the nuclei of the material are torn off and the gas becomes a mixture of free electrons and positively charged ions. Such an ionized gas is termed a *plasma*. Except for the fact that it is gaseous, a plasma has many things in common with a metal such as copper. In particular, both are excellent conductors of electricity, a fact we noted earlier in our discussion of magnetohydrodynamic power generation.

The principle of magnetic confinement of a plasma can be illustrated by the example of what is sometimes called a "magnetic bottle." An idealized version of such a bottle is sketched in Fig. 7. We imagine that in some way a plasma has been created within the region surrounded by the magnetic field lines of the coil. Recall that this plasma is a gas composed of ions and electrons. Let us consider now what might happen if either an electron or an ion tried to get out of the plasma region by crossing the magnetic-field lines.

It is a fundamental law of electromagnetism that when a charged particle moves across a magnetic field, a force F (called the Lorentz force) is exerted on the particle in a direction perpen-

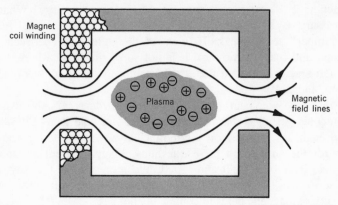

Figure 7. Confinement of a hot plasma by a magnetic field "bottle."

dicular to both the magnetic field B and the velocity v of the particle, as shown in Fig. 8. The equation, which is the consequence of Ampere's Law, reads

$$F = qvB$$

where q is the charge on the particle, taken positive for an ion. The units here are mksc (meter-kilogram-second-coulomb), but that need not concern us now. It is in fact this law which explains the electric field and current produced in a magnetohydrodynamic generator or in a wire conductor when it is moved across the magnetic field of an electric generator.

When a charged particle tries to cross a magnetic field line, the Lorentz force F acts in such a way as to make the particle circle around the line. Electrons circle in one direction and positive ions in the other, but both are trapped by the field lines and are unable to cross them. Ideally, then, the only way the particles can move unimpeded is along the field lines. They may leak out the ends of the bottle, but we can minimize the leakiness of our bottle-stoppers by forcing the magnetic field lines closer together there. Even better, we can eliminate the ends of the bottle altogether by joining them to form a torus, or doughnut. In practice, the confinement of a plasma by a magnetic field involves additional complex processes, but the basic ideas are the same.

Magnetic confinement makes it possible to isolate a hot ionized

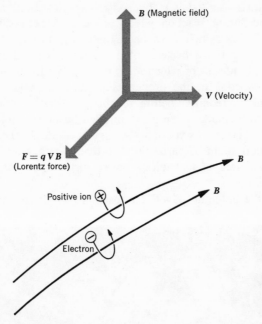

Figure 8. Forces on moving ions and electrons in a magnetic field.

gas from the material walls of a container. Without magnetic confinement, there would be no hope for controlled thermonuclear power, because no material is known which can withstand the temperatures necessary for the fusion reaction.

In addition to its confinement function, the magnetic field may be used to heat the plasma. We may imagine the field lines in Fig. 7 to behave in much the same way as a bundle of rubber bands under tension, being bulged outward by the pressure of the plasma which they surround. If the magnetic field strength is increased, a procedure equivalent to increasing the tension in the hypothetical rubber bands, the field lines will tend to become straighter. The volume surrounded by the field lines is thus decreased and the plasma within this volume is compressed and heated. This process, which is called *magnetic pumping,* is incorporated in more complex forms in many of the thermonuclear devices currently being investigated.

Scientists are today still a very long way from achieving a controlled fusion reaction which produces a net-positive energy yield. Schemes which have been tried, and ideally should have worked, have failed because of a variety of complicated plasma phenomena, not all of which are yet understood. Much additional basic knowledge of the properties of ionized gases in magnetic fields will be required before reliable predictions of plasma behavior can be made. Even if a controlled fusion reaction should be achieved, there are as yet only the vaguest of ideas concerning how the reaction might be harnessed to provide useful work. This is an entire new area of technology whose surface has not even been scratched.

But the potential payoff for fusion power is tremendous, and

Figure 9. Increased demand for high-temperature nuclear fuel materials has led to the investigation of the physical properties of a number of metal and ceramic fuels at temperatures up to 3000°C. In the vacuum chamber shown in this photograph, measurements are made on samples by heating them to high temperatures. Properties such as melting point and emissivity are determined with this equipment. (Ewing Galloway)

justifies the effort which is being expended upon it today. The supply of deuterium in our oceans is limitless; thus fusion power would represent a truly permanent solution to man's energy needs. Moreover, fusion reactors are not expected to produce significant amounts of radioactive waste, so that with them one would not have the waste-disposal problem which will surely be a major problem of the next centuries if fission-reactor power takes over the present role of coal power. If one wished to indulge in some long-range speculation, one might imagine a civilization of the future in which all energy came from the sea; fusion-power-produced electricity and fuel cells run on hydrogen produced electrolytically from sea water. It is amusing to contemplate that the ocean, which was the cradle of life on this planet millions of years ago, might thus someday be man's ultimate sustainer.

The Role of the Engineer

Our discussions of some of the proposed energy-conversion devices of the future have led us through a wide range of scientific and technological subject areas—from biological photosynthesis through steam turbine technology and electrochemistry to nuclear and plasma physics. When faced with the awesome body of scientific knowledge which is represented by all these areas, one may well wonder whether the engineer as we know him today is not a vanishing breed whose functions will gradually be taken over by physicists, chemists, and representatives of other basic sciences. To such a question the answer must be that this is assuredly not the case—quite the contrary—if anything, the particular and special talents of the engineer will be needed more than ever before if our future energy needs are to be successfully met.

What distinguishes the engineer, however scientifically or research oriented he might be, from the "pure" scientist is that the engineer has the ultimate goal in mind of building something or making something work, or of making something work better than it has before, or of manufacturing it more economically. Often the fundamental scientific information necessary to achieve his goal is available, and his function is to assemble and apply this information in an imaginative and ingenious fashion. In many instances, however, the need for additional fundamental understanding may lead the engineer along the path of "basic" research. Though he may then at times appear indistinguishable from the pure scientist, there remains the important difference that at the end of the trail the engineer perceives, however dimly, an object, device, or system that his efforts may help to perfect.

Many of the energy-conversion systems we have discussed are reasonably well understood in regard to the basic physical phenomena which govern their operation, although in some cases important gaps in our understanding still exist. Yet almost all of these devices are still in the laboratory stage. Some undoubtedly will remain there permanently. Engineering developments and technological advances will be the decisive factors in determining which of these devices ultimately emerge from the laboratory and come into general use. And engineers will surely play key roles in these developments and advances. But to do so, engineers may have to cross many of the traditional boundaries which have in the past compartmented the engineering profession. Tomorrow's engineer may have to be part chemist, part physicist, part electrical, mechanical, and civil engineer, if he is to cope with complex systems such as those we have been discussing. For today's engineer, whatever his interest, there remain countless challenging design problems associated with the ever-changing complexion of the energy system we now use, which is such an important part of our entire economy.

The space program being pursued by the United States today affords us a good preview of the possible shape of things to come in power systems engineering. With the exception of thermonuclear power, all the energy-conversion devices we have discussed here, and many others that we have not had space to mention, are under active study and development in the search for power sources to meet the special needs of space exploration. For this reason, though his goals are in the sky, the space engineer's most significant victories may in the end be celebrated here on earth.

Bibliography

Austin, L. G., Fuel Cells, *Scientific American,* vol. 201, no. 4, pp. 72–91, October, 1959.
Ayres, E., and C. A. Scarlott, "Energy Sources: The Wealth of the World," McGraw-Hill Book Company, New York, 1952.
Lansdell, N., "The Atom and the Energy Revolution," Philosophical Library, Inc., New York, 1958.
Putnam, P. C., "Energy in the Future," D. Van Nostrand Company, Inc., Princeton, N.J., 1953.
Skrotzki, B. G. A., and W. A. Vopat, "Power Station Engineering and Economy," McGraw-Hill Book Company, New York, 1960.
Space Electrical Power, *Astronautics and Aerospace Engineering,* vol. 1, no. 4, May, 1963.

APPLICATIONS

1. Read the full version of Archibald A. Hill's "What Is Language?" (Appendix B), and identify as many different kinds of paragraph development as you can.

2. What proportion of Hill's paragraphs may be said to consist essentially of definition? What proportion of them use other methods of paragraph development? What does the comparison suggest about the writer's problem of defining a thing?

3. How many different methods of paragraph development do you find in "Energy Sources and Energy Conversion"? Contrast your findings with those of "What Is Language?"

4. Identify a dozen transitional devices bridging the paragraphs of "Energy Sources and Energy Conversion." Do you find any that are present by logical implication only and not in so many words? Are they effective?

5. Take an example of your own writing and review the opening paragraph, the closing paragraph, and several central ones with reference to the guidelines set forth in the text.

6. Using the same example, review your transitions from paragraph to paragraph. Where a transition is missing, write one in. If the overall result seems mechanical, try for more variation in your transitional devices, or—what is more difficult—imply them clearly.

PART 3

Your Subject

6 | Saying What You Mean

To come right out with it, we must now consider some problems of grammar. Technically grammar consists of two broad divisions: *accidence,* which has to do with the forms of words (he *runs* an experiment; she *ran* an experiment; they are *running* an experiment), and *syntax,* which has to do with the ways words are put together in sentences. By contrast, when a PTA member says, "They ought to teach more grammar in the schools," she is probably thinking of a child's remark such as "Pop ain't got no chewin' tobaccy." The PTA member's comment has little to do with either accidence or syntax. Rather, it concerns the question of usage— which in this case happens to be the common usage of the group to which the child belongs. If "Pop ain't got no chewin' tobaccy" is really an offense,[1] it is an offense against sensibility, not against sense. No failure of communication is possible; no native speaker of English could have the slightest doubt about what the child meant. Of course we would not suggest that any technical presentation should be written in Grammar II, but we will still not spend very much time on usage.[2] For that matter, we will not spend much time on the technical aspect of grammar either. Our overriding concern will be with those aspects of grammar that are most important to writers as aids to getting on with the job—especially those aspects with which many technical writers have difficulties.[3]

We shall therefore immediately define some terms that we will use frequently in the discussions that follow. Of course there are dozens more that modern students of English use in talking about their specialties, but we will not need them here. If you are interested in pursuing them, you can turn to a number of sound modern discussions.[4] For the present, the following definitions are all you will need.

Grammar. We have said that the study of grammar consists of the study of the forms of words (accidence), and the ways words are put together in sentences (syntax). This means that the study of grammar lies entirely within the framework of the sentence. If you can write consistently good sentences, you are well on your way to a mastery of expository writing.

Sentence. A sentence is a grammatically complete statement. To be a complete statement, it must contain a subject and a finite verb, that is, a verb that is capable of making an assertion. The subject may be modified in a number of ways (for example, by adjectives), and the verb may also be modified (for example, by adverbs); the verb

---

1 Some modern students of language do not consider such usage to be really a mistake at all; they simply distinguish it from "cultivated speech" (Grammar I) by calling it Grammar II.

2 Excellent handbooks are available to which the student can refer for counsel on usage. See, for example, Bergen Evans and Cornelia Evans, *A Dictionary of Contemporary American Usage* (New York: Random House, 1957).

3 H. J. Tichy of Hunter College, City University of New York, has analyzed a hundred papers on chemical engineering and has found that at least half of the "mistakes and weaknesses" involved sentence structure ("Engineers Can Write Better," *Chemical Engineering Progress,* 50 [February, 1954], 104–107).

4 Ralph M. Albaugh, *ENGLISH, A Dictionary of Grammar and Structure* (San Francisco: Chandler, 1964); J. N. Hook, *Hook's Guide to Good Writing* (New York: Ronald, 1962); R. W. Pence and D. W. Emery, *A Grammar of Present-Day English,* 2nd ed. (New York: Macmillan, 1963).

may also be followed by a complement, a word or phrase that completes the meaning of the verb. A sentence may also be regarded as consisting of two parts only: the *subject* (including all modifiers) and the *predicate* (including the verb and its modifiers and the complement and its modifiers).

Clause. A clause is a group of words that contains a subject and a predicate. When it stands alone, however, it is called a simple sentence—not a clause. If it is a part of a sentence containing more than one clause, it will be either a main clause (because it does not function as a noun, an adjective, or an adverb) or a dependent clause (which also contains a subject and a predicate, but which cannot convey meaning by itself because it functions as a single part of speech).

Phrase. Like a dependent clause, a phrase is a group of words that functions as a single part of speech, but it does not have a subject and a predicate.

Part of Speech. Parts of speech are words that perform particular functions in sentences. They have been classified into four groups:

1. Nouns and pronouns (conveniently called substantives), which name;
2. Adjectives and adverbs, which qualify;
3. Verbs, which assert;
4. Prepositions and conjunctions, which connect.[5]

Groups of words can also perform the same functions as parts of speech.

So much for technical grammar. We turn now to some important principles of clear statement.

The Psychological Bottleneck

The first principle of clear statement requires you to make sure that every sentence you write says *exactly* what you mean. Unfortunately, it is not often that this can be done in a first draft. Clear sentences do not flow from the pen like molten metal into a mold; they must be roughed out, and shaped, and ground, and polished. There are good psychological reasons why most of us must suffer through every step of this refining process before we have actually

5 Pence and Emery, *op. cit.*, p. 5.

said what we meant to say. A. J. Ayer, Grote Professor of Philosophy in the University of London, has put it by analogy:

Of course, the people who talk of having difficulty in putting thought into words are describing something that actually occurs. . . . But I think that we shall be misunderstanding the character of this fact if we conceive it as being analogous to a man's going to his tailor and trying to get a suit to fit him; as if the thought were already there, fully-fledged, and it were just a matter of finding words to clothe it. The thought which we are unable to put into words is vague and inchoate; the symbols in which it is embodied are fragmentary; they do not fit together, or not in any way that satisfies us. As we find more appropriate expression for it the thought itself becomes more definite. In the end, one may say "Yes, that is what I meant all along," but the fact is not that one had the meaning all along, which the different sets of words more or less faithfully reflected, as an artist may make several attempts at a portrait, with his model in front of him, before he gets the likeness that he wants. In this case there is no such model. The words say "what we meant all along" because it is they that finally give its sense to the whole previous process of groping; we are satisfied with them in a way that we were not satisfied before.[6]

In a similar vein, Harold Martin and Richard Ohmann of Harvard and Wesleyan University point out a paradox in the processes of knowing and telling. One does not *know* until he has *told,* however he may try to sidestep the issue with the rationalization: "I *know* what I mean, but I can't find the words to express it." Martin and Ohmann say:

There is something attractive about this simple account of a baffling matter. But the account is probably a misstatement or at least an overstatement. It would be more accurate to say, "I know very vaguely what I mean, but so vaguely that I can't find any words inclusive enough to represent the notion I have of what I think I know." Put in those terms, the resolution of the paradox is closer. If we begin to describe an experience by testing one series of words after another, rejecting or altering as we do so, gradually the vagueness of our understanding diminishes as "wrong" words are eliminated and as "right" or "nearly right" words are accepted as the proper symbols of the experience. We are directed by a vague understanding of the experi-

6 A. J. Ayer, "What Is Communication?" in *Studies in Communication* (London: Secker & Warburg, 1955), pp. 23–24.

ence to words roughly suitable for its expression; by testing a variety of words which are roughly suitable, we refine our understanding of the experience. Thus we come to know the shape of experience through the process of using words to describe it. . . . We have had the experience before we begin to express it; we *know* or understand it only when we find means to transform it, internally or externally into some symbolic pattern.[7]

From the standpoint of the working professional writer, the late Bernard De Voto, long-time editor of *Harper's Magazine,* said:

A writer needs years of the daily discipline of the desk before he can say anything well enough so that in a third or fourth revision it will passably represent what he wants it to and will be sufficiently clear for the reader to get what he means.[8]

Perhaps, then, our statement on the first page of this book that a writer should know his subject now seems deceptively simple. Of course he should know it—in the ordinary sense that he has mastered his subject background. But he cannot really know it until he can tell it. When he can—when he has found means to "transform it . . . into some symbolic pattern"—he will discover an unanticipated benefit. The real payoff lies in the converse. Having told about his subject, the writer knows it far better than he did before. He writes a technical report because the boss wants it; at the same time, he pockets dividends in the form of sharpened knowledge and insight into his own specialty. This is like winning the daily double at the race track.

Predication

You can make the fastest strides toward achieving clear expression by *keeping the lines of your predications straight.* With a few minor exceptions, every sentence you will write will contain two essential parts: the *subject* and the *predicate.*[9] The subject is the

---

[7] Harold C. Martin and Richard M. Ohmann, *The Logic and Rhetoric of Exposition* (New York: Holt, Rinehart and Winston, 1963), p. 2.

[8] Bernard De Voto, "What Counts Is the Job," in A. S. Burack, ed., *The Writer's Handbook* (Boston: The Writer, 1959), p. 55.

[9] See pp. 140–141.

thing, the event, or the idea that you intend to talk about. The predicate is what you intend to say about it. If you keep these two elements uppermost in mind, you will find it hard to go far wrong in writing a good English sentence. But how often our minds lead us astray! Look at the following sentence written by an experienced professional engineer:

In order to acquire prominent use by the rank and file electronics engineer, the research physicist first had to obtain a knowledge of the electronic action involved, and then a whole new field of solid state physics and metallurgy was expanded.

This may seem to be an unfair example because we do not know what the preceding sentence said or what followed; and the context of the paragraph in which the sentence stood is missing. Nevertheless, it is justifiable to ask that every sentence stand on its own feet. This one falls flat on its face.

Read it again. Can you identify the subject—what the writer intended to talk about? Can you identify the predicate—what he intended to say about it? If you think you can, you may be putting words into the writer's mouth; you may be making your own interpretation of what you think he meant to say, and you could be very wrong. In what kind of apparatus was this *electronic action* going on? You might guess that it was in a transistor. One term that follows, *solid state physics,* would tend to support that guess. How about *metallurgy* then? Does that confirm the notion that the writer is talking about transistors? Or does it suggest that he is talking about the strength of materials from the standpoint of defects in crystal structure? Any guess would be hazardous. In short, this is the kind of sentence that—literally—drives directors of research to seize the telephone and instruct the personnel manager to "remind me to deny any salary increase for Dr. X."

What can be done about sentences like this? John Halverson and Mason Cooley have given an instructive example:

A . . . student, writing about political campaign methods, says:
  "The use of the father image can be carried back to early United States history."
This is not just a little haywire; it is scarcely intelligible. How can you "carry back" such a "use"? The writer was thinking, as it turned

out, of such things as the early designation of George Washington as the father of his country, and reasoning that the modern exploitation of a candidate's fatherly appearance might not be new in all respects. Yet, as it turned out, he also did not mean that the Founding Fathers ever consciously used their paternal characteristics for political purposes. What *was* his subject then? What he wanted to talk about was the appeal or effectiveness of the so-called "father image." *That* was not new. Obliged to re-examine the basic predication of his sentence, the student was able to untangle both his syntax and his thought, and write:

> "The father image had as much appeal in the early days of the Republic as it does now, but only in modern times has that appeal been so systematically exploited in political campaigns."

The result of his close attention to predication was not just an intelligible sentence but the actual discovery and articulation of what he had had "in mind" only vaguely.

A practical guide, then, to meaningful predication is that the "something spoken of" should be clearly formulated and made the grammatical subject of the clause; what is said about it should be exactly stated and should be the predicate of the clause.[10]

To repeat: *always keep the lines of your predications straight.*

Some Sentence Patterns

To increase your facility in building effective sentences, you should know the principal classifications in which they normally occur. A familiar classification is based on the possible combinations of independent and dependent clauses that they contain.

The core of all writing is the *simple* sentence. A simple sentence may contain any number of modifiers (except clause modifiers), and thus it may turn out to be quite long and appear quite complicated; but if it contains just one independent clause, it is still a simple sentence. Consider Figures 6.1 and 6.2.[11] Notice that the skeletons of these two sentences are identical irrespective of the added modifiers. We could add even more modifiers and still retain the simple-sentence form.

[10] John Halverson and Mason Cooley, *Principles of Writing* (New York: Macmillan, 1965), pp. 50–51.

[11] These sentence diagrams are of the Reed and Kellog type, first published in 1877 and by turns in and out of favor since then in American schools. As

H₂S | stinks

Figure 6.1. H₂S stinks.

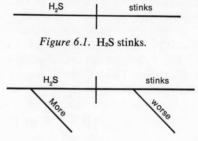

Figure 6.2. More H₂S stinks worse.

Of course a monotonous succession of short sentences would sound like a child's primer, but simple sentences can be expanded in a variety of ways to yield a more mature style. The most obvious way of expanding a simple sentence is by compounding one or more of the elements within it. By doubling or trebling the subject or the predicate (or either part of the predicate), we can add a second or third full idea to a simple sentence without writing a separate one. Look at the following examples:

Intellectual curiosity is necessary for successful research work. Industrious application is also necessary.

Combine the two sentences to form a *compound subject* (Figure 6.3).

The geologist interviewed the holders of the claims. He examined the entire staked area. He scrutinized records in the county clerk's office.

Combine the sentences to form a *triple predicate* (Figure 6.4).

The physiologist dissected the cells of the ganglion. Then he froze the cells.

Combine these to form a *compound verb* (Figure 6.5).

---

recently as 1963, a widely used college-level textbook had made a persuasive case for the ease with which grammatical relationships can be grasped through the use of such diagrams (Pence and Emery, *op. cit.*). Because engineers and scientists are at home with drawings of all kinds, the present author has not been surprised to find that a few sentence diagrams give them quick insight into sentence structure. The important conventions to bear in mind in reading these are that a heavy base line represents a main clause, a full vertical line separates a subject from a predicate, and slant lines show modifiers.

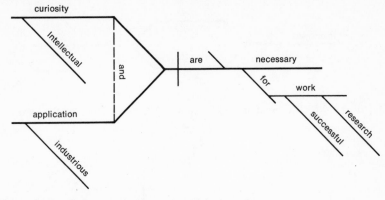

Figure 6.3. Intellectual curiosity and industrious application are necessary for successful research work.

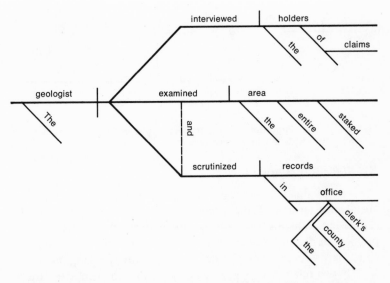

Figure 6.4. The geologist interviewed the holders of claims, examined the entire staked area, and scrutinized records in the county clerk's office.

The chancellor asked nonstudents to stop the sale of *Spider*. He also asked the dean of students to consult with members of SLATE.

Combine these to form a *compound complement* (Figure 6.6).

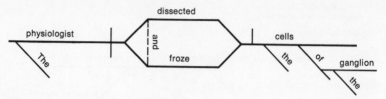

Figure 6.5. The physiologist dissected and froze the cells of the ganglion.

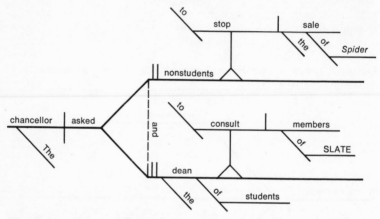

Figure 6.6. The chancellor asked nonstudents to stop the sale of *Spider* and the dean of students to consult members of SLATE.

Relationships Among Ideas

Next to predication for clear writing is the expression—in unmistakable terms—of the proper relationships among ideas. In expressing thoughts that are at all involved, the writer has the problem of dealing with several main ideas at once. In the simplest case, there will be two main ideas, and broadly speaking, there can be only two relationships between them: either the two ideas are of about equal importance, or one will be plainly more important than the other. The grammar of our language provides a number of ways by which these relationships can be made clear to the reader.

The way to show that two ideas are of equal importance—when they should be dealt with in a single sentence—is to express them as *main clauses,* that is, as groups of words that contain both a subject and a predicate and that could otherwise stand alone as separate sentences. Thus:

> She came, I saw, she conquered.—J. N. HOOK

Here are three main clauses, each of which could stand by itself as a separate sentence but which are obviously more effective as written.

When two ideas are of unequal importance, the more important one is expressed as a main clause, and the less important one is expressed as a *dependent clause*. For example:

> If we now consider light spreading out from a small source, we see immediately that in the corpuscular aspect the number of photons will decrease with the distance in exactly the same way as does the energy of the wave in the undulatory aspect.—MAX BORN

It will be obvious that various combinations of main clauses and dependent clauses are possible. Sentences that contain two or more main clauses but *no* dependent clause are called *compound sentences*. The quotation by Hook, above, is a compound sentence, as are the two following examples.[12]

> The principles are understood in the abstract, and the facts are understood in respect to their embodiment of the principles.—A. N. WHITEHEAD

> Language is a household invention and we must not expect it to be applicable very far beyond the confines of household experience. —D. H. WILKINSON

Sentences containing one main clause and one or more dependent clauses are called *complex sentences*. The quotation by Born, above, is of this type, and so are the two following.

> When any body exists in the elastic state, its ultimate particles are separated from each other to a much greater distance than in any other state.—JOHN DALTON

> As I have said on former occasions, Harley Street is the grave—shall I not say cemetery—of clinical research.—SIR CLIFFORD ALLBUTT

12 Be careful not to confuse a compound sentence with a simple sentence containing a compound predicate, like that shown in Figure 6.5.

Sentences containing two or more main clauses and at least one dependent clause are called *compound-complex sentences.* Here is an example that, though rather short, is still in the compound-complex pattern.

The air was very dry, and my paper curled so badly that it was inconvenient to write on.

Compound-complex sentences may also be long and involved as in the following example.

For convenience it is usual to take as the peak loading the maximum gas pressure in the cylinder and to neglect the amelioration of that pressure by the inertia of the piston, and since a motor vehicle engine is constantly called upon to operate at maximum torque and at quite low speed, this is a reasonable assumption, but in the case of marine, stationary, or aero-engines, which can exert full torque only at relatively high speed, the inertia of the pistons and connecting-rods reduces substantially the peak loading, and this consideration should be taken into account.—SIR HARRY R. RICARDO

EXERCISE

Consider carefully the ideas that Ricardo expresses in this sentence and the relationships that he shows among them. Now rewrite the passage so that the compound-complex sentence is broken down into simple sentences, compound sentences, and/or complex sentences, in any combination you choose. Has your version gained in clarity? Or do you prefer the compact style of the original? Why? What of the reader who may be encountering this subject matter for the first time?

Coordination and Subordination

When two ideas are of about equal rank, the grammatical relationship that the writer shows between them is said to be one of *coordination,* and he usually expresses this relationship in one of two ways: by using a *coordinating conjunction,* or by using a *logical connective.* Here are some common ones:

COORDINATING CONJUNCTIONS	LOGICAL CONNECTIVES
and	however
but	therefore
or	nevertheless
nor	so

When one idea is less important than the main idea, the relationship is often shown grammatically by using subordinating words, which may be either subordinating conjunctions or relative pronouns. Here are some of the commoner ones, though there are many more, as well as many other ways of showing subordination.[13]

SUBORDINATING CONJUNCTIONS	RELATIVE PRONOUNS
when, if	who
after	which
since, as	that
so that	

Faulty Coordination

We have become so accustomed to hearing coordinating words that the moment one appears, we expect a statement of equal value to follow. And when we hear a subordinating word, we immediately foresee a minor statement. If, then, the writer follows a coordinating word with a minor statement, the reader will be thrown off the track. The obvious remedy is to anticipate the minor idea by using a subordinating word. Some examples follow.

Faulty coordination: Meyerson called for a new look in education, *and* it involves a departure from the Hutchins philosophy.

Effective subordination: Meyerson called for a new look in education *that* involves a departure from the Hutchins philosophy.

Weak coordination: I had been warned about the radiation hazard, *but* I carelessly entered the posted area.

[13] See, for example, Baxter Hathaway, *Writing Mature Prose* (New York: Ronald, 1951), pp. 13–44, *et passim*.

Effective subordination: Though I had been warned about the radiation hazard, I carelessly entered the posted area.

Placement of Subordinate Elements in the Sentence

A subordinate construction (whether it happens to be a clause or a phrase) is usually weak when it is put at the end of a sentence, where it sounds like an afterthought. It is usually best to avoid such an anticlimactic effect by putting subordinate constructions first. For example:

Weak: Today's moon race is a waste of the taxpayers' money, in my opinion.

Better: In my opinion, today's moon race is a waste of the taxpayers' money.

Weak: We might have lost World War II if Fermi had not stolen some space in a squash court.

Better: If Fermi had not stolen some space in a squash court, we might have lost World War II.

A Horrible Example

To produce the following example, this author has emasculated a passage by two fine writers by stripping it of the grammatical pointers that showed the relationships among the ideas of the original.

Some ancient cathedrals inspire solemnity and awe. They have a consecrated purpose. Visitors are curious. They speak in hushed voices. Whispers reverberate through the nave. Echoes come back. They bear messages of mystery. The labor of many architects and artisans has been forgotten. The scaffolding has been torn down. Their mistakes have been erased. Their mistakes have been hidden by dust. This dust has been there for centuries. We see that the finished whole is perfect. We are impressed. The agency may have been superhuman. Sometimes we enter such an edifice. We may do this when it is only partly built. We hear the sound of hammers. We smell the reek of tobacco. We hear jests. We realize that these are great structures. These structures are the result of something. Ordinary human effort has built these buildings. This effort must have been directed. It must have had some purpose.

EXERCISE

Rewrite this horrible example by showing explicitly what you feel to be the right relationships among the ideas, using devices for coordination and subordination. Your first attempt may be rough. No matter. Smooth it out in a second rewrite. Then compare your best version with the original, which appears on pages 30–31.

Summary

For improvement in technical writing, our interest in grammar is purely pragmatic—in those elements of it that will be most helpful in achieving clear presentation. Clear predication is achieved when the writer has made sure of the exact thing he wants to talk about and has made that his grammatical subject and when he has determined exactly what he wants to say about that subject and has made that his grammatical predicate. The proper relationships among ideas are made clear to the reader by grammatical coordination of ideas of equal importance and by grammatical subordination of ideas of lesser importance.

7 | Sense and Non-Sense

This chapter discusses a gaggle of sentence faults. Each of these has been found to be ubiquitous in technical writing. Probably you can commit a few without inflicting fatal damage to your technical communication, but more than a few can drop a well-organized basic structure to the level of non-sense. Even one really conspicuous fault strikes the reader like a fly on an angel food cake.

Even so small an error as a single misprint can throw the reader off if it occurs in a prominent place. For example, a well-known textbook has a misprint on the first page. The book is an excellent one, and you might think that a single misprint would be taken by the reader in stride. Not so. The present author has used this book in his own classes and has seen students waste incredible amounts of time wondering whether the word was actually mis-printed—and, if not, what the sentence meant! Another text says—again on page 1—that a research chemist is interested in studying "all the kinds of carbohydrates found in natural petro-leum." Of course the chemists in the class know that there are no carbohydrates in petroleum—natural or otherwise—(unless a practical joker has put sugar in someone's gasoline tank) and that the intended word was *hydrocarbons,* not *carbohydrates.* Never-theless, an error of this sort can waste much reader time.

Moreover, once a reader has spotted such an error, even though it be trivial, he will be suspicious of everything else the writer has to say. The writer is then in the unenviable position of a football team trailing 28–10 going into the fourth quarter. He is forced into playing a catch-up game.

Now these two errors—a misprint, and a mistake in fact—are not quite the same as the sentence faults that we will be discussing, but they illustrate the traps that a writer can dig for himself if he does not keep a sharp eye out for slips of every kind.

Let us now look at some of the writing faults that disturb executives in technically based industries. For example, the Gen-eral Electric Company has issued an educational publication en-titled *General Electric's Answer to . . . WHY STUDY ENG-LISH?* The management of this leading company thought the answer important enough to justify printing half a million copies for distribution to schools, counselors, and interested individuals. What writing problems of young engineers do General Electric executives speak of? Here is their story:

A Problem in Expression

The top engineer upstairs is on the telephone. He says to us: "Right before my eyes is a brief report made by one of your young engineers. I have to guess what the fellow is driving at. I'm no English shark, but I find myself getting a little angry when I see four sentences tied together with commas. He has *principle* for *principal,* and he has also misspelled *accommodate* and *Cincinnati.* What if some of this fellow's bad sentences get into the hands of our customers?" . . .

The top engineer is wound up. "At the last meeting of our Associa-tion, representatives of all the major companies complained about the way their younger men were putting down their words—and futures—on paper. Can't someone tell us what to do?"[1]

Now just what writing faults is this top engineer "a little angry at"? He names two specific classes of errors and one general class that in itself covers a multitude of sins:

1. Comma fault
2. Misspelling
3. Bad sentences generally

The top engineer says further that the representatives of all major companies complain about such errors. In the light of such evidence, this entire chapter will be devoted to a discussion of these faults and how to avoid them. As you face the tasks of writing term papers, graduate theses and dissertations, industrial technical reports and memorandums, and papers for publication in professional journals, you should thumb the chapter often. For here you will find ways to correct most of the slips that most of your superiors would otherwise blue-pencil.

The Nonsentence

The *nonsentence* is also called a *sentence fragment* because it lacks one or more of the parts of a complete sentence. It is often used in everyday speech, as, for example, in answer to the question "What's in the big concrete building on The Hill?" The fragment "The bevatron" would be entirely appropriate. But in technical writing, the nonsentence is nearly always out of place. When it does occur there, it gives the impression that the writer does not know what a sentence is. For example: "The engineer misplaced the decimal point in his stress calculation. Much to his chagrin." This fragment should be either combined with the preceding sentence or rewritten as a part of another one.

When a predicate complement[2] is detached from its verb to form a sentence fragment, the fragment should simply be reunited

[1] *General Electric's Answer to . . . FOUR WHY'S* (Schenectady, N.Y.: General Electric Company, 1958), p. 6.

[2] A *predicate complement,* sometimes called a subjective complement, is anything (noun, adjective, phrase, or clause) that completes the meaning of the predicate by describing or renaming the subject of the verb.

with its verb: "Our plan was to visit Woods Hole Marine Biological Laboratory. And then to drive west to Scripps at La Jolla." *Remedy:* "Our plan was to visit the Woods Hole Marine Biological Laboratory and then to drive west to Scripps at La Jolla."

Another kind of nonsentence results when a verb is omitted: "The doctor anxiously scanning the cardiograph chart and hoping that the fibrillation would subside." *Remedy:* Insert the verb. "The doctor *was* anxiously *scanning* . . ."

The Siamese Sentence

Analogous to the Siamese twins Chang and Eng, the *Siamese sentence* consists of two separate sentences unnaturally joined together. Sometimes they are run together without any punctuation at all, like this: "The examination for the Professional Engineer's License starts at eight o'clock it lasts all day." Here are two separate sentences run together without so much as a pause for breath, and for this reason the construction is sometimes called a *run-on sentence.* In the foregoing example, the simplest remedy is to put a semicolon after *o'clock.* Or you could make two sentences by putting a period after *o'clock* and capitalizing *it.* Or you could put a coordinating conjunction after *o'clock* and perhaps strike out *it.* Any of these repairs would satisfy a copyreader, but you might do still better by recasting the whole thing.

The Comma Splice

When the independent clauses of a Siamese sentence (see above) are separated by a comma, the error is called a *comma splice* or *comma fault.* "The Apollo disaster was not our first space-related tragedy, three technicians were killed in 1964 when a solid fuel rocket went wild." Grammatical analysis will show that this example is really two sentences in one. However, if you are uncertain about this, try reading the example aloud. Each of the two parts before and after the comma will sound complete in itself, and you will immediately recognize that we have two independent clauses here. These could be separated in any of the ways mentioned in connection with the Siamese sentence. Better yet, look at both clauses and decide whether they are of equal importance. If you think not, try subordinating the less important one.

Agreement of Subject and Verb

Everyone knows that a subject and its verb should agree in number. If the subject is singular, the verb should be singular; if the subject is plural, the verb should be plural. In practice, however, two situations can trick the unwary. The first of these occurs when a singular subject is followed by a phrase whose last noun is plural. In this case, there may be some temptation to follow the plural noun with a plural verb; for example, "The average gestation period of elephants *are* twenty months." The subject, *period,* is singular; the verb should be *is.* A somewhat different problem arises when an individual is referred to in two capacities: "The *chemist* and *Nobel laureate* was chairman of the symposium." The two elements of the subject refer to a single person, and the singular verb *was* is correct.

An apparent anomaly of our language is that we have singular nouns that can be used in the plural sense and plural nouns that can be used in the singular sense ("The *news was* sent out to every paper on the AP wire"). A safe general rule in such cases is to use the verb form that agrees with the sense of the subject—not with its grammatical form. But there are exceptions and variations that are beyond the scope of this discussion.

If you aspire to a management position in your profession, you will have to write a great deal, and you might as well plan right now to do the job as efficiently and well as you can. It would be a good investment to get an authoritative handbook[3] and keep it beside your dictionary.

The Subjunctive Mood of the Verb

The *subjunctive mood* of the verb expresses:

1. Statements contrary to fact: "If I *were* a millionaire, I should endow . . ."

---

[3] Such as Bergen Evans and Cornelia Evans, *A Dictionary of Contemporary American Usage* (New York: Random House, 1957).

2. Statements that make a concession: "Even though the special theory of relativity *be* true, certain observations remain unexplained."

3. Statements expressing a wish: "I wish I *were* better able to handle symbolic logic."

Most authorities on usage concede that the subjunctive mood is disappearing from our spoken language and being replaced by the simple indicative. In edited writing the subjunctive is still preferred; and in technical writing, which seeks to offer the reader the clearest grammatical clues to meaning, it is often the only way to say what you mean. As an experiment, try any other form of the verb *to be* in example 3 above, and note what happens to the meaning.

Confused Pronoun Reference

Confused pronoun reference is a neat trick for tying the reader up in knots. It is quite versatile, too, because there are at least three ways to do it.

1. *Leave out any antecedent,* that is, anything to which the pronoun might refer. Like this: "Accurate calculation is the way *it* is calculated by all conscientious engineers." *What* is calculated? What does *it* refer to? There is no antecedent here to give the reader a clue. *Revision:* "All conscientious engineers stress accuracy in calculation."

2. *Give a wrong antecedent.* "We returned the instrument supplied by the *manufacturer that* was not sufficiently sensitive." *What* was not sufficiently sensitive? *Revision:* "We returned the manufacturer's *instrument that* was not sufficiently sensitive."

3. *Let the same pronoun refer to several possible antecedents.* "The Guggenheim Fellow planned to visit both Brown and Pittendrigh. *He* thought *he* would tell *him* about new findings on fiddler crabs, and *he* could also see the work *he* was doing on fruit flies." *Revision:* Try this as an exercise. Can you straighten it out yourself, or would you have to ask the writer what he actually intended to say?

Wrong Pronoun Case

It is not often that a native speaker of English will use a pronoun in the *wrong case,* with one exception. That one is good for at least an hour's argument at any cocktail party. Should you say, "Between you and *me* . . . " or "Between you and *I* . . . "? The English teachers present will point out that *between* is a preposition, that prepositions always take the objective case, and that the pronoun has to be *me*—to which some collector of quotations will reply, "Then why did Shakespeare write, 'All debts are cleared between you and I'?"[4] He may even go on to quote authorities who say that "between you and I" cannot even be classed as a mistaken attempt to speak "elegant" English. Nevertheless, the authorities do agree that "between you and I" is not standard English and certainly should be avoided.

The same rule holds when the *you* of these examples is replaced by a phrase: "A massive concrete shield stood between the TRIGA reactor and *me.*"

Howlers

When a modifier is so placed in a sentence that it has no apparent word to modify or when it modifies the wrong word, it is said to *dangle. Dangling modifiers* can cause such ludicrous effects that *howler* is an apt term for them. In "Having said that he thought the thesis was poor, a quick vote was taken," we have no idea who did the saying.[5] The late Harold Ross, long-time editor of *The New Yorker,* might have written in the margin, "Who he?" The remedy is therefore to identify *he: "Having said* that he thought the thesis was poor, the *professor* asked for a quick vote."

When a dangler modifies the wrong word, something like this results: "Splattered with soap from a bursting reactor kettle, the chemists refused to clean up the laboratory." The *chemists* were not splattered—the *laboratory* was. And the chemists refused to clean it up because they were forbidden to touch animal fat by religious code. Possible revision: "The bursting reactor kettle

---

4 This wisecrack proves nothing, because our language is changing all the time; some four centuries have passed since Shakespeare's day, when the word *nice* meant *effeminate.*

5 On quick reading, the sentence merely seems vague. But grammatical analysis would show that the sentence actually says that *the vote* did the saying. This is worse than a vague statement; it is dead wrong.

splattered the laboratory with soap, but the chemists refused to clean it up." Question: Is this the best possible revision? Is the pronoun *it* now guilty of confused reference? Try a rewrite of your own.

Sometimes a misplaced verb will give an effect somewhat like that of a dangling modifier: "The wind blew over the desert where the corpse lay and whistled."[6] A mechanical correction for this would be to move the verb close to its subject: "The wind blew and whistled over the desert where the corpse lay." Still, on reading this over, we see that it is wordy and that a sharper statement would be "The wind whistled over the desert where the corpse lay."

Squinting Modifiers

In technical writing, where the critical aim is to avoid ambiguity, the *squinting modifier* is even worse than the *howler*. You can usually figure out what the writer of a howler meant to say. Not so with the squinting modifier. It can be interpreted to modify either the idea that precedes it or the idea that follows it, and there is no way of telling which. "Doctoral candidates who fail their preliminaries *quickly* are discouraged." Quickly *fail* or quickly *discouraged?* Future doctoral candidates would lose less sleep if the writer had put *quickly* either before *fail* or before *discouraged.*

Only

Herman M. Weisman has pointed out how critical to precision in technical writing is the accurate placement of the word *only*. He gives the following examples of the shifts in meaning that occur when this one word is moved around.

a. Only the physicist calculated the value of X in the equation.
b. The physicist only calculated the value of X in the equation.
c. The physicist calculated only the value of X in the equation.
d. The physicist calculated the only value of X in the equation.

6 The author has been unable to identify the source of this delightful howler, but its perpetrator deserves thanks and an apology.

e. The physicist calculated the value of only X in the equation.

f. The physicist calculated the value of X only in the equation.

g. The physicist calculated the value of X in the only equation.[7]

If you were alert when you read sentence f., you noticed that *only* squints in both directions. Read the sentence aloud, and you will see that the meaning depends on whether you pause after X or after *only*. There is no way to distinguish the two meanings in the written version, and revision is a must.

Illogical Predication

We have already discussed the general principles of clear predication in the previous chapter. A more specific problem is involved in the illogical *"something is something else"* construction. Here are three examples: "Water is one of California's most pressing problems." (*Water* is not the problem. Water shortage or lack of adequate distribution facilities or lack of desalination plants may be, but not water *per se*.) "Precision is when you carry out the calculation to three decimal places." (Precision does not denote time; the statement makes no sense, and should be rewritten.) "Nuclear engineering is where the fundamental assumptions are derived from the equation $E = mc^2$." (Nuclear engineering does not denote place; again the sentence should be rewritten.)

Illogical predications like those of these examples are so common in all kinds of writing that you should be alert to spot them in your own and shoot them down.

Changing Horses in Midstream

Mixed sentence structure results when a writer starts with one sentence pattern and then shifts to another midstream. "The older engineers now admit that in their undergraduate days how irresponsible they were." The usual cause of this awkwardness is simple carelessness, and the remedy is to revise the sentence. "The

[7] Herman M. Weisman, *Basic Technical Writing* (Columbus, Ohio: Merrill, 1962), p. 323.

older engineers now admit how irresponsible they were in their undergraduate days."

The Flat Adverb

Hardly a month goes by without someone writing a letter to an editor complaining about signs like "Drive *slow* and see our town; drive *fast* and see our jail." In this warning *slow* is not a misused adjective, it is a flat adverb; that is, an adverb that does not end in *-ly*. Ralph M. Albaugh lists seven dozen of the commonest flat adverbs, some of which have no forms in *-ly* and some of which do and can be correctly used as adverbs either with or without the *-ly*.[8] In technical writing the *-ly* form is preferable when there is a choice.

Unnecessary Shifts

When you have decided on a particular method of approach to any technical presentation, stick to it throughout the entire piece. Use consistent pronouns. If you start by addressing the reader as *you*, stay with it; do not shift to *one* for the sake of variety. Do not shift the tenses of your verbs unless you have a good reason for doing so and unless you give your reader fair warning. Do not shift your verbs back and forth from the active to the passive voice; and use the active voice as often as you can without violating professional propriety.

Think of the effect on the reader of unnecessary shifts by analogy with the sum of a series of vectors (see Figure 7.1).

Faulty Parallelism

Faulty parallelism occurs when elements that are joined by a conjunction are not parallel in grammatical structure. "To listen to classical music and playing chess are diversions many scientists enjoy." This mixed construction could be avoided by using either

[8] Ralph M. Albaugh, *ENGLISH, A Dictionary of Grammar and Structure* (San Francisco: Chandler, 1964), pp. 74–75.

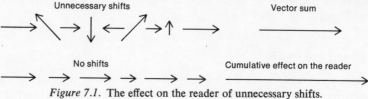

Figure 7.1. The effect on the reader of unnecessary shifts.

the infinitive or the gerund in both phrases. Probably the latter sounds more natural: "Listening to classical music and playing chess are diversions many scientists enjoy."

Un-English Idiom

Idiom, in the sense we shall speak of it here, is "the syntactical, grammatical, or structural form peculiar to a language: the genius, habit, or cast of a language."[9] The more characteristic "forms" of interest in technical writing are word groupings and word order. For example, in a German textbook, we may read, *"Die Cellulose ist in Wasser und verdünnten Saüren ungelöslich."* If we retain the idiomatic German word order in a translation into English, we get, "The cellulose is in water and dilute acids insoluble." Of course no native speaker would write such a sentence in English, but there is one typically Germanic word order that has come into wide use in American technical writing. The reason for this may arise from a mistaken notion that it gives an economical form of statement. Or T. R. Henn may have given a more probable explanation:

In a recent paper in *Nature* (176, p. 851, November 5, 1955) J. R. Baker has drawn attention to the use of "Germanic" English in scientific papers—that is, "the piling up before a noun of words that are not adjectives, but are used adjectivally." The writer traces this to the fact that so many scientists now writing, particularly in the U.S., are of German descent, to whom this construction comes naturally. In German it is, of course, justified and made practicable by the far more

[9] *Webster's Third New International Dictionary, Unabridged* (Springfield, Mass.: Merriam, 1964).

complex system of case endings; in English it can give rise, if not to confusion, to extreme ugliness.[10]

You can find examples of such confusion and ugliness in the titles of papers given in the table of contents of almost any professional technical journal you happen to pick up. Here is a random selection:

Frequency Independent Antennas
Randomly Oscillating Turbulent Channel Flows
Chemically Prestressed Concrete Hyperbolic Paraboloid Shell Model
Synchronous Machine Stability Enhancement with State-Space Switching
A 3.5 db-Noise-Figure, S-band, Medium-Power, Injected-Beam, Crossed-Field Amplifier

These may indeed represent economical statement—for the writer. But, to quote Richard Brinsley Sheridan, "Easy writing's curst hard reading."

APPLICATIONS

1. You are the editor of an internationally respected American technical journal. Would you accept for publication without change the five titles of papers just quoted? If not, how would you rewrite them?

2. The following example is offered partly for your amusement and partly to illustrate the wide differences between two languages of idiom in words, word groupings, and word order. It is an essentially verbatim report that a noted foreign-born scientist made to his chief, Walter J. Hund.[11] Read it through, and then rewrite it in the idiom of American English.

I just returned from San Francisco—see—I got my trousers full of rain. I saw X and had the chance to kill two flies with one thing. X surely has the nick-nack to quickly grapple things like that. We talked about Y. You know the trouble I have been having with Y. I have

10 T. R. Henn, *Science in Writing* (New York: Macmillan, 1961), p. 240.
11 Personal communication: Walter J. Hund to this author, December, 1945.

always given him a down dressing every year twice. But this time I was out put by his having completely looked over something important I gave him to do. I said to him, "Y, if you are not more careful I shall have to over look these matters again myself." Well, Y and I had a good chit-chat and then I made a bicker with him. The shot up of it all was that he will try to do more good in the future.

3. Select a rather long example of your own writing—a technical paper, a technical memorandum, or a technical report. Underline all the sentence faults that you find in your example, and rewrite them along the lines suggested in this chapter. Keep this revision; we will return to it at the end of the next chapter.

8 | The Case for the Lively Corpse

If you have come this far in the book and have put forth some effort on the applications with each chapter, you should now be able to write a workmanlike English sentence. You will have in mind shortcuts to clear predication and to expressing relations among ideas. You will also know how to cut from your first drafts a variety of sentence faults that hinder communication with your reader.

But if you aspire to real excellence in your writing, these efforts are not enough. A series of merely workmanlike sentences may lie as "dead" copy. "All that [their writers] utter is stillborn, without life or interest, their sentences . . . laid out like so many stiffs, end to end."[1] Fortunately, though, such sentences may be made to live, to breathe, even, sometimes, to dance.

How does the writer bring this about?

He does it chiefly by turning his attention from the grammatical attributes of his sentences to their rhetorical effects.

Before we look at rhetorical effects, we must clear up any possible misunderstanding of the word *rhetoric* as we shall use it here. In this author's classes, the mere mention of the word has drawn scornful glares from some technical men. *Rhetoric* has brought to mind the "hidden persuader" in his gray flannel suit, mocking intellectual honesty and twisting the language into whatever form he thinks will sell the most supercrunchies.

Such a reaction is half right. In England, *rhetoric* is used in a disparaging sense, to mean the use of exaggeration or display to serve the ends of the writer rather than to benefit the reader. In the United States, however, it "still means primarily the art or science of the specially literary uses of language . . ."[2] This is the sense in which we shall use it here.

In the Evanses' definition, rhetoric is alluded to as both an art and a science, and one implication of this is that using it effectively is not easy. It is not. Neither is any other skill worth having. Generation after generation of writers have bled over the difficulties, and generation after generation of them have thought that the effort was worthwhile. We have already cited Charles Darwin's struggles with his prose. Other writers have described similar syndromes.

I

A sentence and a worm are the most stupid of animals and the most difficult to teach tricks.[3]

II

William James, who wrote a great deal and who wrote very well, once remarked that "everything comes out wrong with me at first." But, he

---

[1] Walter S. Campbell, *Writing Non-Fiction* (Boston: The Writer, 1949), p. 73.

[2] Bergen Evans and Cornelia Evans, *A Dictionary of Contemporary American Usage* (New York: Random House, 1957), p. 425.

[3] T. E. Hulme, English critic, quoted by Thomas S. Kane and Leonard J. Peters, *A Practical Rhetoric of Expository Prose* (New York: Oxford, 1966), p. 245.

went on, once he had his composition in a crude shape he could "torture and poke and scrape and pat it until it offends me no more." . . . As James implies, it is often frustrating; but when one has tortured and poked and scraped his work into shape and knows at last that he has succeeded in saying what he set out to say, then the satisfaction is very great.[4]

III

The step from writing simple sentences that are grammatically correct to writing sentences that are original in thought and language is a tremendous one. . . . For the original management of language involves the growth of the total intellect. This is a slow process. It is a word-by-word process, sustained by devoted attention to language, rather than by ambitious attempts to apply abstract principles of rhetoric and construction to large bodies of fact or theory. If, for example, a student is to write about the ideas in an essay by Walter Lippmann, he must be able to think with the concepts that are in the language of Walter Lippmann, and this is a very large order indeed; for Lippmann's prose results from a lifetime of thinking about words and of thinking with them.[5]

So much for the difficulties and the rewards. We now turn our attention to a planned procedure designed to set your feet on the path to excellence. This procedure can be divided into two parts: writing and reading.

For rapid improvement in *writing* techniques, you must become familiar with the rhetorical forms of sentences and sentence sequences. From your *reading,* your improvement will be more like the physical process of osmosis; or, to change the metaphor, your ideas about how to write well will simply rub off as you read fine prose.

Rhetorical Sentences

From a rhetorical standpoint (as opposed to the grammatical), sentences are usually divided into four classes: the *loose sentence,* the *periodic sentence,* the *interrupted sentence,* and the *balanced*

---

[4] *Ibid.,* pp. IX–X.
[5] Charles Child Walcutt, *An Anatomy of Prose* (New York: Macmillan, 1962), p. XIII.

sentence. The first three are classes of individual sentences. The so-called balanced sentence, however, is often a sequence of two sentences that balance each other in various ways. We shall see how these work in the examples that follow.

THE LOOSE SENTENCE

The loose sentence is the rhetorical type with which we are most familiar. It is typical of conversation, and it may, in fact, be the only kind of sentence you will find in informal writing. In the loose sentence, the subject and the verb are stated early, and then whatever modifiers, qualifications, or exceptions that the speaker thinks worth mentioning are added. Sometimes these thoughts may seem to be—or may actually be—afterthoughts. The characteristic of a loose sentence that will enable you to spot it on sight is that it is grammatically complete before the final period. Often you could end it at several different points, like this:

On the other hand, the scientists believe that the literary intellectuals are totally lacking in foresight,/ peculiarly unconcerned with their brother men,/ in a deep sense anti-intellectual,/ anxious to restrict both art and thought to the existential movement.—C. P. SNOW, p. 5.[6]

You will note that this sentence would have been grammatically complete immediately before each virgule (/). As it stands, it gives a feeling of an easy, conversational flow of thought.

THE PERIODIC SENTENCE

In contrast to the loose sentence the periodic sentence withholds its main thought until the end. Its arrangement is thus climactic, and when used sparingly, it can be very striking:

In 1933, four years before his death, Rutherford said, firmly and explicitly, that he didn't believe the energy of the nucleus would ever be released—nine years later, at Chicago, the first pile began to run.—C. P. SNOW, p. 33.

[6] This, and the following examples not otherwise identified, are from Sir Charles P. Snow's *The Two Cultures: And a Second Look* (London: Cambridge University Press, 1963), originally delivered as the Rede Lecture at Cambridge in May, 1959, under the title "The Two Cultures and the Scientific Revolution."

The danger in using the periodic sentence is that it can be overdone, like putting too much garlic in the salad. A skilled orator seldom shouts at the top of his voice, and then only for occasional emphasis. You can probably count the number of clearly identifiable periodic sentences in the fifty-one pages of *The Two Cultures* on the fingers of one hand.

THE INTERRUPTED SENTENCE

The interrupted sentence introduces a parenthetical thought into a conventional sentence pattern. In our daily conversation we use interrupted sentences all the time. Try replaying a tape of any dinner chatter, and you will find that most of the sentences are interrupted ones (and not always by the first speaker). In edited writing, however, interrupted sentences are used sparingly—perhaps not more than two or three in 5,000 words. *The Two Cultures* contains a striking example. After Snow has set the stage by saying that he had been privileged to have a ringside view of one of the most wonderful creative periods in all physics, he writes this interrupted sentence:

And it happened through the flukes of war—including meeting W. L. Bragg in the buffet on Kettering station on a very cold morning in 1939, which had a determining influence on my practical life—that I was able, and indeed morally forced, to keep that ringside view ever since.—C. P. SNOW, pp. 1–2.

THE BALANCED SENTENCE

Balanced sentence is the common term for the rhetorical device next on our list. Sometimes it is indeed just one sentence, with the two balancing elements separated by a semicolon or colon. Perhaps more often, we find two sentences. In either case, the characteristic that makes the device effective is that two ideas of about equal importance are balanced in parallel grammatical structure.

As a group, the scientists . . . are inclined to be impatient to see if something can be done: and inclined to think that it can be done, until it's proved otherwise. This is their real optimism, and it's an optimism that the rest of us badly need.

In reverse, the same spirit, tough and good and determined to fight it out at the side of their brother men, has made scientists regard the other culture's social attitudes as contemptible. This is too facile: some of them are, but they are a temporary phase and not to be taken as representative.—C. P. SNOW, p. 7.

Rhetorical Sentence Sequences

In addition to rhetorical sentences themselves, there are two kinds of rhetorical sentence sequences that we must consider. These are *variety in sentence length* and *parallelism*.

VARIETY IN SENTENCE LENGTH

In previous chapters we have considered several aspects of the effects of sentence length on the reader. Two further examples will suggest the range of variation to be found in good writing. The first is from Charles Darwin's *Origin of Species,* where he discusses "organs of extreme complication and perfection" and concedes at once that the idea of an eye developing by natural selection would be hard to believe. "To suppose that an eye," he says, "with all its inimitable contrivances for admitting different amounts of light, and for the correction of spherical and chromatic aberration, could have been formed by natural selection, seems, I freely confess, absurd in the highest degree." But after some paragraphs designed to prepare the reader's mind for a startling new concept, he makes the point—in a sentence of nearly one hundred words—that the idea is not so hard to believe, after all.

When we reflect on these facts, here given much too briefly, with respect to the wide, diversified, and graduated range of structures in the eyes of the lower animals; and when we bear in mind how small the number of all living forms must be in comparison with those which have become extinct, the difficulty ceases to be very great in believing that natural selection may have converted the simple apparatus of an optic nerve, coated with pigment and invested by transparent membrane, into an optical instrument as perfect as is possessed by any member of the Articulata Class.[7]

[7] Charles Darwin, *The Origin of Species* (New York: Modern Library, 1936), Chapter 6.

For examples of short sentences the works of Ernest Hemingway and John Steinbeck naturally come to mind. Here is a paragraph from one of Steinbeck's early books:

The night was clear. Pilon had emerged from his hard daily shell, as he did now and then. He was the idealist tonight, the giver of gifts. This night he was engaged in a mission of kindness.[8]

This is fiction. It is not offered as a model for technical writing but simply to show how effective short sentences can be *if they say something.*

The more usual use of the short sentence is for occasional emphasis, to produce an effect of force and impact following a series of longer sentences. Here is an example that discusses the writing problems of scientists in industry.

Now I must consider the scientist in industry, who is not doing research but who is applying his scientific or engineering knowledge to practical ends. Occasionally I am asked to advise industrial organisations about the reports their applied scientists and engineers are writing. The samples sent for my inspection demonstrate clearly that something is wrong. Grammatical and syntactical faults abound. A superficial examination would lead the critic to conclude that a short revision course in English grammar and some remarks on style appropriate to their apparent needs would meet the situation. *It does not.*[9]

These examples illustrate some ranges of sentence length. Of course you can find longer ones, say in Milton (1641), John Locke (1689), Henry James (1888), or as recently as Edmund Gosse (1923). You can also find many one-word "sentences" in the modern staccato style. But these extremes have no place in technical writing. A norm characteristic of mature professional writing is not hard to find in contemporary prose. For example, the average sentence lengths in samples of Louis Bromfield, Bernard De Voto, Walter Lippmann, Joseph Wood Krutch, and Arthur M. Schlesinger, Jr., have been found to be about twenty-six words.[10]

---

[8] John Steinbeck, *Tortilla Flat* (New York: Covici, Friede, 1935), p. 126.
[9] B. C. Brookes, "The Teaching of English to Scientists and Engineers," in Randolph Quirk and A. H. Smith, eds., *The Teaching of English: Studies in Communication 3* (London: Secker & Warburg, 1959), p. 144.
[10] Verna L. Newsome and Enola Borgh, *Sentence Craft* (New York: Macmillan, 1952), p. 144.

Still, as we pointed out as early as Chapter 2, average sentence length tells only a fraction of the story of effective communication.

PARALLELISM

Parallelism is one of the most useful rhetorical devices that you can use to enhance the clarity of your technical presentations. The power of the method is so great and its possibilities are so various that we can do no more than suggest them here. If you refer to one of the standard texts on rhetoric for fuller discussion, your time will be well spent. By way of introduction, the following brief summary is offered.

Parallelism is one of the most important of rhetorical principles. Differences between good and bad writing and between one kind of prose style and another can often be traced to differences in the handling of parallel structures. So long as the writer is using parallelism functionally—that is, to communicate unornamented thought— he can hardly overdo it. . . . The function of parallelism is to increase clarity by showing the proper relationships between coordinate ideas."[11]

For an example of the effective use of parallelism, we turn to the memoirs of Herbert Hoover. In spite of the legendary struggles that Hoover had with English composition during his student days at Stanford, we see here an appropriate and effective use of parallel structure to "show the proper relationships between co-ordinate ideas."

The great liability of the engineer compared to men of other professions is that his works are out in the open where all can see them. His acts, step by step, are in hard substance. He cannot bury his mistakes in the grave like the doctors. He cannot argue them into thin air or blame the judges like the lawyers. He cannot, like the architects, cover his failures with trees and vines. He cannot, like the politicians, screen his shortcomings by blaming his opponents and hope that the people

11 Baxter Hathaway, *Writing Mature Prose* (New York: Ronald, 1951), p. 91. For the fuller discussion suggested above, see particularly Chapter 9, "The Fundamentals of Parallelism," and Chapter 19, "The Rhetorical Effects of Parallel Structures."

will forget. The engineer simply cannot deny that he did it. If his works do not work, he is damned.[12]

Sentence Rhythm

Rhythm is a quality that sentences either have or lack; it would be more descriptive to say that they have rhythms that are either pleasing to the ear or harsh and discordant. One would be hard put to support an argument that technical writing should strike the ear like the prose of E. B. White. On the other hand, there is no reason why it should set the reader's teeth on edge. Consider the following passage:

Between the sunlit surface waters of the open sea and the hidden hills and valleys of the ocean floor lies the least known region of the sea. These deep, dark waters, with all their mysteries and their unsolved problems, cover a very considerable part of the earth. The whole world ocean extends over about three-fourths of the surface of the globe. If we subtract the shallow areas of the continental shelves and the scattered banks and shoals, where at least the pale ghost of sunlight moves over the underlying bottom, there still remains about half the earth that is covered by miles-deep, lightless water, that has been dark since the world began.[13]

That passage has rhythm. It delights the ear in precisely the way that Robert Louis Stevenson had in mind when he said that the writer's "pattern, which is to please the supersensual ear, is addressed throughout and first of all, to the demands of logic."[14] The general reading public thought so, too, about *The Sea Around Us,* because it went into eleven printings the year it was published.

Now just what is it that gives its quality to such prose? Can you analyze it? Of course it is partly a matter of sentence rhythm. But even the analysis of prose rhythm has given some very serious

[12] Herbert Hoover, *Memoirs of Herbert Hoover,* Vol. I: *Years of Adventure* (New York: Macmillan, 1951), pp. 132–133.

[13] Rachel L. Carson, *The Sea Around Us* (New York: Oxford University Press, 1951), p. 37.

[14] Robert Louis Stevenson, "On Some Technical Aspects of Style in Literature," in Lane Cooper, ed., *The Art of the Writer* (Ithaca, N.Y.: Cornell, 1952), p. 320.

scholars some very knotty problems.[15] Nor is rhythm by any means the full answer to the effectiveness of the late Miss Carson's prose. In the final analysis, this answer can only be your own. Probably you can approach it best by reading all her books—not selections culled by anthologists—but *all* of them.

Reading for Writers

Finally, we come to the most enjoyable phase of the discipline to which you should commit yourself if you wish to write really well. This task, in short, is *reading*—but reading with an open mind and a sympathetic ear. It is not even suggested that you read analytically, although you may do so if you wish. If you do, you can go all the way with Mortimer J. Adler and never read anything unless you are seated at your desk, pencil and paper at the ready, prepared to end up with a sheaf of notes after each sitting.[16]

No.

For our present purposes, what we are speaking of here is reading through which you can apprehend what good writing is and develop a consciousness, at least in the back of your mind, of some of the methods of the masters.

This process has been cogently pictured by Langley Carleton Keyes in one of the most popular articles ever to be published in the *Harvard Business Review*.[17] Keyes suggests a one-foot shelf of books through which the reader can "have it made . . . writing and editing with new knowledge, clearness, force, and freshness. . . . Once a management man has launched himself on this reading project—once he has really committed himself to it—I promise him that he will find it a great adventure, with a big pot of gold at the end. I have seen it happen."[18]

[15] See, for example, Wayland Maxfield Parrish, "Prose Rhythm," in *Reading Aloud* (New York: Ronald, 1953), pp. 483–506.

[16] Mortimer J. Adler, *How to Read a Book* (New York: Simon and Schuster, 1940).

[17] Langley Carleton Keyes, "Profits in Prose," *Harvard Business Review*, 39 (January–February, 1961), 105–112.

[18] Keyes' one-foot shelf of books consists of the following: *The Elements of Style*, by William Strunk, Jr., and E. B. White; *English Prose Style*, by Herbert Read; *A New Way to Better English*, by Rudolf Flesch; *Walden*, by Henry David Thoreau; *The Education of Henry Adams*, an autobiography; *Treasure Island*, by Robert Louis Stevenson; *The Forsyte Saga*, by John Galsworthy; *The Bridge of San Luis Rey*, by Thornton Wilder; *Grapes of Wrath*, by John Steinbeck; *The*

This chapter concludes our discussion of sentences, but it cannot end without calling your specific attention to Henry David Thoreau. You will look far to find a text on English composition or rhetoric that does not make reference to Thoreau as a master sentence maker. In "Profits in Prose," Keyes puts it this way:

If you read Thoreau's *Walden* when you were a freshman in college— or if you have never read it at all—read it now. It certainly ranks among the ten greatest books ever written in this country. It has averaged a new edition every year for over 100 years. And among other things you will find that Thoreau has never been surpassed in his mastery of the English sentence.[19]

APPLICATION

Take up the example of your own writing that you revised as suggested in Chapter 7, Application 3. As you read it over, you will probably notice that most of your sentences are "loose sentences," as we defined them in this chapter. Do you find any periodic sentences, interrupted sentences, or balanced sentences? If not, try writing in a few, here and there, and then draw your own conclusion about the effectiveness of your revisions. What of the variations of your sentence lengths? Have you a few really long ones, fact-packed but reading in a conversational tone? And a few short snappy ones where you need special emphasis?

Have you overlooked any potential parallel constructions? Give this your closest attention, and then *show* your reader the logical parallels that are inherent in your material.

Read a few paragraphs of your copy aloud. Do you sense a pleasing rhythm? If not—if the flow sounds jerky—fix the content of a few paragraphs in mind, and then dictate the way you would *say* it into a tape recorder. You may be pleasantly surprised at the outcome.

Old Man and the Sea, by Ernest Hemingway; *The Summing Up,* by W. Somerset Maugham; *The Second Tree from the Corner,* by E. B. White; *The Years with Ross,* by James Thurber.

[19] Keyes, *op. cit.,* p. 111. Of the Thoreau editions that Keyes mentions, you would be well pleased with the Modern Library Edition, which contains other writings in addition to *Walden;* edited and with an introduction by Brooks Atkinson (New York: Modern Library, 1937, 1950).

9 | Lightning or the Lightning Bug?

Mark Twain said that writing should be easy because you just put down words in rows on paper, and all the words are in the dictionary. The irony of the remark is sharpened when we compare it with two other Twain quotes about words. In his essay on William Dean Howells he said, "A powerful agent is the right word. Whenever we come upon one of those intensely right words in a book or newspaper the resulting effect is physical as well as spiritual, and electrically prompt." Twain carried the electrical analogy still further: "The difference between the right word and the almost right word is the difference between lightning and the lightning bug."

Two centuries before Twain, Jonathan Swift wrote, "Proper words in proper places make the true definition of style."

So far in this book we have been talking about the proper places. Now, we must talk about the proper words. In technical writing, choosing the word that exactly expresses your intended meaning is imperative. "Technical writing" that uses words that are vague, inexact, or misleading is not technical writing at all. It is worse than useless. In our space age an inexact operating instruction for a rocket may lead to the loss of equipment worth millions of dollars and to the snuffing out of lives, which is all the more tragic because it is so needless. Your objective in technical writing is not to write so that you can be understood, but to write so that *you cannot be misunderstood.*

The use of words in technical writing may be considered from two points of view: first, the qualities of words, and second, the choice of the right word.

The Qualities of Words

The first and obvious quality of words is that they have meaning. This is a vast subject to which you could devote a lifetime if you were so inclined;[1] but our assumption here is that you will be a professional scientist or engineer and that your chief aim will be to get on with the job. We shall therefore limit ourselves to three important aspects of word meaning in relation to technical presentations. Specifically, these are the denotative and connotative meanings of words, their general and specific meanings, and their abstract and concrete meanings.

DENOTATION AND CONNOTATION

The *denotation* of a word is the minimum of definition that is needed to indicate what it means; and this requires specific refer-

[1] For a brief introduction you might glance at the following: C. K. Ogden and I. A. Richards, *The Meaning of Meaning: A Study of the Influence of Language upon Thought and of the Science of Symbolism* (New York: Harcourt, Brace & World, 1962); Leonard F. Dean and Kenneth G. Wilson, *Essays on Language and Usage* (New York: Oxford University Press, 1963); Kenneth G. Wilson, R. H. Hendrickson, and Peter Alan Taylor, *Harbrace Guide to Dictionaries* (New York: Harcourt, Brace & World, 1963).

ence to the physical object, entity, or idea to which the word refers. Thus, the denotation of a word has nothing to do with any attitudes, emotions, or associations that may come to mind in connection with it. In contrast, the *connotation* of a word includes all of the evaluations, reactions, and emotional experiences that anyone may associate with it.

The denotative meaning of a word, therefore, will be essentially the same for most of us, and the connotative meanings can be as wide and varied as the experiences of every individual. The word *mother* has the *denotation,* simply, of "female parent." For most of us, it has the *connotations* of love, comfort, warmth, safety, and a host of other impressions. For young Mrs. Barbara Smith Johnson, according to Truman Capote, it connoted ". . . never anything nice to wear or enough to eat."[2]

A short dictionary definition of a word is essentially denotative. The word *lobster,* for example, has been defined as follows:

1. any of the various large, edible, marine, stalk-eyed, decapod crustaceans of the family *Homaridae,* esp. of the genus *Homarus.* 2. the spiny lobster (which see). 3. any of various similar crustaceans, as certain crawfishes. . . .[3]

For the present author, the word *lobster* connotes, among many other associations: broiled lobster on Cape Cod, before a visit to the Marine Biological Laboratory at Woods Hole; an undergraduate laboratory experiment that failed because not enough lobster shells could be gathered to identify an organic compound found in them; "lobsters" that are not lobsters at all, but rather Pacific crayfish, though they are called lobsters throughout the Pacific area; Honolulu dinners featuring them stuffed with diced ham, bacon, green pepper, and rice; the depreciation of the value of the dollar, because such dinners once cost 50 cents; spearfishing for lobsters in azure coral caves on the windward side of Oahu; and so on and on.

Such a variety of connotative meanings that a word may bring to the mind of the reader is simply one of the occupational hazards

---

2 Truman Capote, *In Cold Blood* (New York: Random House, 1965), p. 185.
3 *The American College Dictionary* (New York: Random House, 1966).

of a technical writer. To deal with it, you must recognize that it *is* a hazard; define your terms whenever you think there is the slightest chance that your reader may take off in the wrong direction; and choose words that are as free of connotative implications as you can.

GENERAL AND SPECIFIC WORDS

Confining our discussion now to the denotations of words, we may classify words as either *general* or *specific*. Actually, these are relative terms. A general word denotes a large variety, or a large number of classes of specific entities, and a particular word may be so specific that it refers to a unique item. For example, we have arranged a series of words in a spectrum ranging from general to specific like this:

General   **Specific**
Substance—Liquid—Compound—Alcohol—Ethanol—C_2H_5OD

In this spectrum we have not, of course, reached any item approaching a unique specimen, for even though we have made ethanol more specific by replacing one of the hydrogen atoms with deuterium, we know that in such a molecule there can be an almost limitless variety of positions of the electrons. Still, the illustration makes the point that when the time comes to write about C_2H_5OD, the word *alcohol* will not do.

ABSTRACT AND CONCRETE WORDS

Abstract words are words that have no specific referents, and they can mean almost anything to almost anybody. What do *you* mean by *excellence, democracy, truth, intellectual honesty, responsibility of the press,* or even *entropy?* We could spend an evening discussing our own interpretations of any of these—except perhaps *entropy*—and end up further apart than when we started. And even with a term like *entropy,* we might need a semester or a year talking and thinking about it before we could be fairly certain that we were talking about the same thing the next time we used the word.

Concrete words, on the other hand, are words that stand for definite objects or classes of objects that we can perceive with any or all of our five senses. Take *bourbon,* for example. By sight, we observe that it is a liquid, that it is brown, and that when poured into a small glass, it forms a characteristic bead at the interface between the glass and the surface of the liquid. By taste, we know that it is neither Irish nor Scotch. By smell, we distinguish it blindfolded from gin or vanilla extract. By touch, we know that it is neither hot coffee nor cold molasses. Can you *hear* bourbon? Perhaps only by extension, but when your host brings a tray of highballs, the tinkle of ice leaves little doubt of what you are likely to encounter.

It will be perfectly obvious to any technical student that complex technical concepts *cannot* be presented unless the writer can choose freely from abstract words, for the simple reason that many of the concepts of science *are* abstract. This is less true of general words, but situations also arise when certain ideas must be presented as generalities. Granting this, the technical writer cannot escape the conclusion that since he must use some abstract and general words, he is under an even heavier obligation to make all the rest of his words as specific and concrete as he can. Otherwise, he may fail to communicate at all.

In practice, it makes little difference whether he makes a conscious distinction between concrete words and specific words, but in his effort to be clear, he must use as many of both as the nature of his subject matter will allow.

Let us look at two contrasting examples.

I

Strangeness of samples has been shown to lead to relative rejection of products in the comparative absence of clues to a frame of reference within which judgment may take place. Variation in clues selected by judges as a basis for evaluation [leads] to greater inter-judge disagreement. Addition of a functional (utilitarian) basis for judgment tends to reduce relative importance of product physical characteristics as a basis for judgment. In the absence of any judgmental frame of reference reduction in the number of product physical attributes apparent to the judges appears to reduce operation of bases for rejection and increase homogeneity of judgment between subjects; inter-sample discrimination is also reduced.[4]

This purports to be a report of a scientific investigation, though it would be hard to know that, unless you realized that its subject was the testing of special foods for use in military spacecraft. The chief difficulty that the reader has here is that the writer has loaded his presentation with abstract and general words.

In sharp contrast, read the following account of the investigation that revealed for the first time the exact site of the biological clock in any living creature—the common cockroach.

II

Turning then to the midgut tumour story—it was really the result of the same sort of tedious long-term work, although the outcome was a complete surprise. Because biological clocks are so difficult to upset in any way there had previously been no way of discovering what had happened if a clock went wrong. But I thought having found this one clock it might be possible to expose an animal to two clocks running out of time with each other (by transplant methods), and that this might have an effect on the animal similar to that which might occur if a clock were malfunctioning. The whole experiment was an extremely long one, as it meant transplanting neurosecretory cells daily into animals in large numbers—and this is a rather fiddling task. The outcome, as so often happens, was totally unexpected, and since tumours in insects are very rare it was, looking back, surprising that I ever found out what was happening; it could easily have been overlooked. . . .

Not much physical equipment is needed for this sort of work; it really depends on very fine dissecting instruments; and tiny chips of razor blade and forceps made from very fine tungsten wire proved better than anything which could be bought. It is true that Halberg was rather shocked to find that I had done hundreds of mitotic counts without the aid of a mechanical stage on the rather simple microscope I then had, but apart from a bit of strain I do not know that it made a great deal of difference in the end.[5]

At the risk of belaboring the obvious, we may note the differences between "frame of reference within which judgment

---

4 Quoted by Sir Ernest Gowers in Fowler's *Modern English Usage* (New York: Oxford University Press, 1965).

5 Janet E. Harker, Girton College, Cambridge University, England; personal communication, March 28, 1965.

may take place," in example I, and "a rather fiddling task" in example II; "operation of bases for rejection and increase homogeneity of judgment" in example I, and "tiny chips of razor blade" in example II. If you had trouble with "neurosecretory cells" in example II, it was not because Harker used an abstract term when a concrete one would have served. The term is about as specific as you can get in this field, and the reader who has trouble with it needs a dictionary, not a better writer.

Choosing the Right Word

Lexicographers and publishers have spent centuries of scholarly work and millions of dollars to provide us with aids for choosing the right word. Some of the products have been exemplary, and some have been junk. An individual writer can expect to provide himself with no more than a few of the best, and his problem is to make the optimum choice in the light of his own needs. Word guides may be divided into two classes: dictionaries and thesaurus-type books. The working scientist or engineer whose chief responsibility is research, design, production, or technical sales and whose writing assignments consist essentially of memorandums and reports about these activities, may need no more than a standard desk dictionary and a thesaurus. But he should be careful to choose his tools on the basis of some background knowledge of what he can expect from them. Some suggestions on making such a choice are offered in the sections that follow.

DICTIONARIES

Three popular desk dictionaries are suitable for college-level use. These are: *The American College Dictionary* (New York: Random House); *Webster's New Collegiate Dictionary* (Springfield, Mass.: Merriam); and *Webster's New World Dictionary* (New York: World). These differ in various particulars that you might not notice on casual inspection, and it would be worth an evening's time to look through the *Harbrace Guide to Dictionaries*[6] to learn what these differences are. Having made your

6 Wilson, *et al., op. cit.*

choice, look through the front matter and back matter to find out what the book contains in addition to the dictionary proper, and, in particular, *read the editor's suggestions on the efficient use of the book*.

Above equipment provided for general use in many plants and laboratories, humorists post the sign: WHEN ALL ELSE FAILS, READ THE INSTRUCTIONS. With a new dictionary, do not wait for all else to fail. Read the instructions and you will save valuable time.

As a student of engineering or science and even when you have reached professional status, you will probably not want to go to the expense of owning an unabridged dictionary. For words in your own field, you may be inclined to look first in specialized technical dictionaries, many of which are excellent; but sometimes you can look through half a dozen of them without finding the word you want. Following such a search, one is embarrassed to learn that a trip to the library would have turned up the elusive word in the unabridged volume with less loss of time and temper. Still, experience will be your best guide to the most likely source of a specialized technical word, and you should acquire some familiarity with the contents and scopes of such technical dictionaries as the following:

Bucksch, H. *Dictionary of Civil Engineering Construction Machinery and Equipment*. London: Pordes, 1955.

Dictionary of Electronic Terms. Chicago: Allied Radio, 1955.

Foster, John, Jr. *Science Writer's Guide*. New York: Columbia University Press, 1963. This is not a dictionary in the ordinary sense, but it is an invaluable source of meanings suitable for explaining technical terms to the intelligent layman. The lay definitions set forth have all been authenticated by authorities.

Henderson, I. F., and W. D. Henderson. *A Dictionary of Scientific Terms*. Princeton, N.J.: Van Nostrand, 1960.

Herland, Leo Joseph. *Dictionary of Mathematical Sciences*. New York: Ungar, 1954.

James, Glenn, and Robert C. James. *Mathematics Dictionary*. Princeton, N.J.: Van Nostrand, 1949.

Malisoff, W. M. *Dictionary of Biochemistry and Related Subjects*. New York: Philosophical Library, 1956.

Schwartz, Robert J. *The Dictionary of Business and Industry*. New York: Forbes, 1954.

Stoutenburgh, John L. *Dictionary of Arts and Crafts.* New York: Philosophical Library, 1956.

Thomas, Robert C., James M. Ethridge, and Frederick G. Ruffner, Jr. *Acronyms and Initialisms Dictionary.* Detroit: Gale Research, 1965.

Tweney, C. F., and L. E. C. Hughes, eds. *Chambers's Technical Dictionary.* New York: Macmillan, 1958.

THESAURUSES

The word *thesaurus* comes from a Greek word meaning "treasury," and properly used, a thesaurus can indeed be a treasury of words for the writer. The name Roget is almost synonymous with the thesaurus, for the first thesaurus of English words and phrases was published by Peter Mark Roget in 1852, and it has been in print in various editions and under various editorships ever since.

The most convenient of these editions to use is one that is arranged in dictionary form.[7] To find synonyms (and sometimes antonyms), look them up alphabetically, as you would in a dictionary. If the word you are after happens to contain only a short entry, with few synonyms, you will then be directed to a major category containing many more words to choose from. For example, if the word you have in mind is *misfire,* but the few synonyms listed do not suit your purpose, you will be directed to the major categories: FAILURE and MISTAKE. Under these, you will find many words that are far removed from what you have in mind, but you still have a fairly good chance of finding just the word you want.

Like any other book, Roget must be used with discrimination. Two hazards face the careless user of any book of synonyms. The first of these is the temptation to use a longer, perhaps more scholarly sounding word than the one first in mind. Make it an ironbound rule to resist this temptation. Better yet, if you can find a shorter word than the one you started with, use it. The second hazard is that words are not exactly synonymous and the word that seems right when you spot it in Roget may mean something quite different. The obvious remedy is to consult the dictionary if you

[7] For example, Norman Lewis, ed., *The New Roget's Thesaurus in Dictionary Form* (Garden City, N.Y.: Doubleday, 1961).

have any doubt at all—and even if you don't, you may be in for an occasional surprise.

A second synonym book that you will sometimes find extremely useful is Norman Lewis' *The Comprehensive Word Guide*.[8] It has many uses, but there is one situation in which nothing else will do: when you have a general idea of what you want to say but can think of no word that suggests just what you have in mind.

Suppose, for example, that you have a particular kind of color effect to describe. If you have ever seen the range of colors produced on a burnished copper surface after it has been exposed to gasoline containing traces of sulfur compounds, you will recognize the problem. In a very rough way, the colors range from jet black through purple, violet, blue, green, and a variety of pinks. The colors vary in intensity. Sometimes they are velvety, and sometimes they are iridescent. The accurate description of these color effects may be critical to a correct interpretation of the effects of the gasoline in internal combustion engines. Your problem is to describe as accurately as possible the color effects on a particular copper test surface.

Here, neither the dictionary nor the standard thesaurus is of much help. Instead, turn to the Index section of *The Comprehensive Word Guide,* and note that you are referred to Color, Category 488. Turning to this, you find the following entries:

488.   COLOR

1. General Color or Coloring, n.

1. **cast** slight amount of color
2. **coloration** combination or pattern of coloring; distinctive color
3. **dye** color produced by dyeing
4. **hue** color
5. **pastel** pale color
6. **pigment** color
7. **pigmentation** coloring
8. **shade** variety or variation of color, esp. toward dark
9. **tincture** tinge
10. **tinge** slight trace of color
11. **tint** pale or delicate color; slight color; trace of a color; shade

8 Norman Lewis, *The Comprehensive Word Guide* (Garden City, N.Y.: Doubleday, 1958).

12. **tone** shade
13. **undertone** subdued color; color changed by the one under it

2. Color Quality, n.

1. **blare** brightness of color
2. **brilliance, brilliancy** degree of resemblance to white or remoteness from black
3. **chroma** quality that combines both hue and saturation; intensity; saturation
4. **hue** variation or modification of color
5. **intensity** sharpness, strength, or purity of color
6. **nuance** shade of difference in color
7. **purity** saturation
8. **saturation** purity of color; degree of remoteness from gray; degree of freedom from mixture with white
9. **shade** degree of color; degree of darkness of a color; intensity
10. **tint** shade
11. **tone** shade

3. Softening or Mellowing of Color Caused by the Passage of Time: patina, n.

4. Play of Colors: chatoyancy, n.

5. The Colors Placed or Mixed on an Artist's Mixing Board: palette, n.

6. Band of Colors Formed When a Beam of Light Is Passed through a Prism: spectrum, n.

7. Effect of Color, Light, and Shade in a Picture: tone, n.

8. Colored; Having Color, adj.

1. **bicolored, bicolor** having two colors
2. **blazing** having bright colors
3. **chatoyant** having a play of colors (chatoyancy, n.)
4. **colorful** full of color; having lots of color; having many or bright colors (colorfulness, n.)
5. **columbine** having the color of a dove
6. **dichroic, dichroitic** showing varying colors in different directions according to how it is viewed, or showing varying colors in two different directions owing to transmitted light—of crystals (dichroism, dichromaticism, n.)

7. **dichromatic, dichromic, dichroic** showing or having only two colors; having two color phases or periods—of certain birds and insects (dichromatism, dichroism, n.)
8. **duotone** in two colors or two tones of the same color
9. **heterochromatic** possessing a variety or complexity of colors
10. **heterochromous** possessing a variety of different colors
11. **homochromatic, homochrome** possessing one color (homochromatism, n.)
12. **homochromous** of the same or uniform color
13. **hued** colored
14. **incarnadine** flesh-colored
15. **iridescent** possessing a variety of colors, or varying colors, like a rainbow (iridescence, n.)
16. **isochromatic** having the same color or tint
17. **isochroous** of the same color or tint throughout
18. **many-colored** having a variety of colors
19. **mellow** full, rich and soft in color (mellowness, n.)
20. **monochromatic, monochroic** containing only one color
21. **motley** varicolored
22. **multicolored** having many, or a variety of, colors
23. **pale** not bright in color (paleness, n.)
24. **parti-colored, party-colored** colored in different tints
25. **pastel** pale in color
26. **piebald** varicolored
27. **pied** containing colors in blotches; varicolored
28. **pigmented** colored
29. **polychromatic, polychrome, polychromic** having, showing, or decorated in a variety of colors (polychromy, n.)
30. **prismatic** highly or brilliantly colored
31. **stellular** colored in starlike spots
32. **trichroic** showing colors in three different directions—of crystals (trichroism, n.)
33. **trichromatic** consisting of, or using three colors (trichromatism, n.)
34. **varicolored** having different colors
35. **varied** marked by a number of different colors (variegation, n.)
36. **variegated** marked in different colors (variegation, n.)
37. **versicolor** changeable in color; having a rainbowlike range of colors; varicolored

9. *Painting or Drawing That Has Only One Color:* monochrome, n. (monochromist, n. monochromic, monochromical, adj.)

10. State of Having Color: coloration, pigmentation, n.

11. Art of Combining Colors: coloration, polychromy, n.

12. Of No Decided or Particular Color: neutral, adj.

13. Pert. to Color, adj.
1. **chromatic** pert. to color or colors
2. **heterochromatic** pert. to a variety or complexity of color
3. **homochromatic** pert. to one color
4. **pigmentary** pert. to color or coloring
5. **tinctorial** pert. or relating to color
6. **trichromatic** pert. to three colors

14. Colors as to Category, n.
1. **achromatic colors** black, white, and shades of gray
2. **chromatic colors** brown, green, red, purple, etc.
3. **fundamental or physiological primaries** red, green, and blue
4. **primary colors** red, blue, and yellow (in painting)
5. **psychological primaries** red, yellow, blue, green, black, and white
6. **secondary colors** colors derived from mixing other colors

15. To Color; To Change or Vary the Color of, v.
1. **discolor** change the color of; change to a different color
2. **dye** give a color to; change the color of
3. **shade** change to a darker or different degree of color
4. **stain** color in a desired way; give color to; discolor
5. **tarnish** discolor
6. **tincture** stain; tinge
7. **tinge** give a slight color to
8. **tint** color slightly
9. **tone** change the color of
10. **tone down** make (a color) less sharp; make less sharp in color
11. **variegate** mark with different colors

16. To Color, i.e., Become Colored, Take On Color, or Become Changed in Color, v. From Sec. 15: discolor, dye, shade, stain, tarnish; Also:
1. **blend** shade into each other (of colors)
2. **tone** take on a color or color quality; agree in color; blend

17. A Coloring: A Changing in, or of, Color, n. From Sec. 15: discoloration or discolorment, variegation; Also: *1.* coloration—act of coloring

18. Change of Color: metachromatism, n.

19. Pert. or Relating to Staining or Dyeing: tinctorial, adj.

20. Discoloration, n.
1. **bruise** discoloration of skin caused by a blow, etc. (bruise, v.)
2. **speck** small discoloration
3. **tarnish** discoloration (tarnish, v.)

21. Discolored, adj.
1. **livid** discolored—of the skin (lividness, lividity, n.)
2. **tarnished** discolored (tarnish, n.)
3. **ustulate** discolored as if by fire or burning

22. Coloring Matter, n.
1. **color** coloring matter
2. **dye** coloring matter used to change color
3. **dyestuff** matter used to dye or change color
4. **lipstick** stick of red or other colored matter used on the lips
5. **mascara** coloring matter used on eyelashes to make them attractive, conspicuous, etc.
6. **pigment** coloring matter
7. **rouge** red powder used as coloring matter; coloring matter used to add a red tinge to the cheeks, lips, etc.

23. To Show Bright Colors: blaze, v.

24. Science of Color, n.
1. **chromatics** science of hue and saturation of color (chromatist, n.)
2. **chromatology** science of color (chromatologist, n.)

25. A Treatise or Essay on Colors: chromatography, chromatology, n.

26. Device for Dealing with Color, n.
1. **chromatometer** device to test one's color perception
2. **colorimeter** device for measuring intensity of color, determining colors, etc. (colorimetry, n., colorimetric, colorimetrical, adj.)
3. **prism** device that separates light into its component colors (prismatic, adj.)[9]

As a preliminary clue to a description of the colored copper surface, you quickly find the entry "488.8.6. *dichroic*—showing

9 From *The Comprehensive Word Guide* by Norman Lewis. Copyright © 1958 by Norman Lewis. Reprinted by permission of Doubleday & Co., Inc.

varying colors in different directions according to how it is viewed,
. . ." This is a fine clue, for it suggests the exact effect that you
see when you tip the copper surface at slightly different angles to
study it. Hopefully you will not use the actual word *dichroic* in
your description, but it has served to indicate a way of thinking
about the effect you must describe.

As you glance through the other entries, you will note that
each of them is followed by a brief notation about meaning—a
helpful provision not to be found in Roget.

Following Category 488, you find the following entries, with
their own lists of synonyms and short definitions:

489. LACK OF COLOR	495. RED
490. BLACK	496. PINK
491. DARK COLOR	497. BROWN
492. BLUE	498. GRAY
493. GREEN	499. WHITE
494. PURPLE	500. YELLOW

Using the suggestions you find among these to support your own
direct observations, you stand an excellent chance of being able to
picture for your reader just what this copper surface looks like.[10]

Spelling

You will recall that one of the mistakes that annoyed General
Electric's "top engineer" (Chapter 7) as much as anything was
misspelled words. In this, he was not alone. The present author
has seen misspelled words cause more executive tempers to flare
than any other gaucherie that a technical writer can commit. The
unvarnished reason for this is that there is no excuse for misspelling. Two remedies are open to anyone. First, there are spelling
rules. *Webster's Seventh New Collegiate Dictionary* gives nearly
fifty of them. You can also find them in many other sources. If you
are blessed with a memory like an elephant, you can keep them all

[10] The example is offered here for illustrative purposes only. It will occur
to you that a report reader might get a better impression of the copper surface
from a color photograph and that he might learn more about the kinds and
amounts of sulfur compounds in the gasoline if he saw the results of a modern
chromatograph. However, we are limiting our discussion to the effective use of
words, and such laboratory methods are beyond our present scope.

in mind—together with the exceptions, which are even more complicated than the rules.

That is the hard way, and it will still not help you spell the names of people and places correctly.

Why not take the second and easy way? If you *know* how to spell a word, go ahead and write it down. If you have the least doubt—and when you do, you will know that too—look the word up. It is as simple as that.

Webster's Third New International Dictionary (unabridged) was published in 1961 and promptly drew criticism from those who felt that in this edition the dictionary had abandoned its place as an "authority" on usage. In "But What's a Dictionary For?" which follows, Bergen Evans defends the approach taken by the editors of the *Third*. After reading it, you will probably agree that a modern technical writer will not go wrong in following current usage.

But What's
a Dictionary For?

Bergen Evans

A specialist in English language and literature, Bergen Evans is professor of English at Northwestern University. He holds the B.A. from Miami University, the M.A. from Harvard, the B.Litt. from Oxford (as a Rhodes Scholar), and the Ph.D. from Harvard. He is the author of The Natural History of Nonsense *(Knopf, 1946),* The Spoor of Spooks *(Knopf, 1954), and with his sister, Cornelia Evans,* A Dictionary of Contemporary American Usage *(Random House, 1957). He has contributed more than 50 articles to* Harper's, Atlantic Monthly, Reader's Digest, *and* Esquire *and has served as moderator of the television word quiz* Down You Go.

THE STORM OF ABUSE IN THE POPULAR PRESS THAT GREETED the appearance of *Webster's Third New International Dictionary* is a curious phenomenon. Never has a scholarly work of this stature been attacked with such unbridled fury and contempt. An article in the *Atlantic* viewed it as a "disappointment," a "shock," a "calamity," "a scandal and a disaster." The New York *Times,* in a special editorial, felt that the work would "accelerate the deterioration" of the language and sternly accused the editors of betraying a public trust. The *Journal* of the American Bar Association saw the publi-

"But What's a Dictionary For?" *Atlantic Monthly,* May 1962, pp. 57–62. Used by permission of the *Atlantic Monthly* and the author.

cation as "deplorable," "a flagrant example of lexicographic irresponsibility," "a serious blow to the cause of good English." *Life* called it "a non-word deluge," "monstrous," "abominable," and "a cause for dismay." They doubted that "Lincoln could have modeled his Gettysburg Address" on it—a concept of how things get written that throws very little light on Lincoln but a great deal on *Life.*

What underlies all this sound and fury? Is the claim of the G. & C. Merriam Company, probably the world's greatest dictionary maker, that the preparation of the work cost $3.5 million, that it required the efforts of three hundred scholars over a period of twenty-seven years, working on the largest collection of citations ever assembled in any language—is all this a fraud, a hoax?

So monstrous a discrepancy in evaluation requires us to examine basic principles. Just what's a dictionary for? What does it propose to do? What does the common reader go to a dictionary to find? What has the purchaser of a dictionary a right to expect for his money?

Before we look at basic principles, it is necessary to interpose two brief statements. The first of these is that a dictionary is concerned with words. Some dictionaries give various kinds of other useful information. Some have tables of weights and measures on the flyleaves. Some list historical events, and some, home remedies. And there's nothing wrong with their so doing. But the great increase in our vocabulary in the past three decades compels all dictionaries to make more efficient use of their space. And if something must be eliminated, it is sensible to throw out these extraneous things and stick to words.

Yet wild wails arose. The *Saturday Review* lamented that one can no longer find the goddess Astarte under a separate heading—though they point out that a genus of mollusks named after the goddess is included! They seemed to feel that out of sheer perversity the editors of the dictionary stooped to mollusks while ignoring goddesses and that, in some way, this typifies modern lexicography. Mr. Wilson Follett, folletizing (his mental processes demanded some special designation) in the *Atlantic,* cried out in horror that one is not even able to learn from the Third International "that the Virgin was Mary the mother of Jesus"!

The second brief statement is that there has been even more progress in the making of dictionaries in the past thirty years than there has been in the making of automobiles. The difference, for example, between the much-touted Second International (1934) and the much-clouted Third International (1961) is not like the difference between yearly models but like the difference between the horse and buggy and the automobile. Between the appearance of these two editions a whole new science related to the making of dictionaries, the science of descriptive linguistics, has come into being.

Modern linguistics gets its charter from Leonard Bloomfield's *Language* (1933). Bloomfield, for thirteen years professor of Germanic philology at the University of Chicago and for nine years professor of linguistics at Yale, was one of those inseminating scholars who can't be relegated to any department and don't dream of accepting established categories and procedures just because they're established. He was as much an anthropologist as a linguist, and his concepts of language were shaped not by Strunk's *Elements of Style* but by his knowledge of Cree Indian dialects.

The broad general findings of the new science are:

1. All languages are systems of human conventions, not systems of natural laws. The first—and essential—step in the study of any language is observing and setting down precisely what happens when native speakers speak it.
2. Each language is unique in its pronunciation, grammar, and vocabulary. It cannot be described in terms of logic or of some theoretical, ideal language. It cannot be described in terms of any other language, or even in terms of its own past.
3. All languages are dynamic rather than static, and hence a "rule" in any language can only be a statement of contemporary practice. Change is constant—and normal.
4. "Correctness" can rest only upon usage, for the simple reason that there is nothing else for it to rest on. And all usage is relative.

From these propositions it follows that a dictionary is good only insofar as it is a comprehensive and accurate description of current usage. And to be comprehensive it must include some indication of social and regional associations.

New dictionaries are needed because English has changed more in the past two generations than at any other time in its history. It has had to adapt to·extraordinary cultural and technological changes, two world wars, unparalleled changes in transportation and communication, and unprecedented movements of populations.

More subtly, but pervasively, it has changed under the influence of mass education and the growth of democracy. As written English is used by increasing millions and for more reasons than ever before, the language has become more utilitarian and more informal. Every publication in America today includes pages that would appear, to the purist of forty years ago, unbuttoned gibberish. Not that they are; they simply show that you can't hold the language of one generation up as a model for the next.

It's not that you mustn't. You *can't*. For example, in the issue in which *Life* stated editorially that it would follow the Second International, there were over forty words, constructions, and meanings which are in the Third International but not in the Second. The issue of the New York *Times* which hailed the Second International as the authority to which it would adhere and the Third International as a scandal and a betrayal which it would reject used one hundred and fifty-three separate words, phrases, and constructions which are listed in the Third International but not in the Second and nineteen others which are condemned in the Second. Many of them are used many times, more than three hundred such uses in all. The Washington *Post,* in an editorial captioned "Keep Your Old Webster's," says, in the first sentence, "don't throw it away," and in the second, "hang on to it." But the old Webster's labels *don't* "colloquial" and doesn't include "hang on to," in this sense, at all.

In short, all of these publications are written in the language that the Third International describes, even the very editorials which scorn it. And this is no coincidence, because the Third International isn't setting up any new standard at all; it is simply describing what *Life,* the Washington *Post,* and the New York *Times* are doing. Much of the dictionary's material comes from these very publications, the *Times,* in particular, furnishing more of its illustrative quotations than any other newspaper.

And the papers have no choice. No journal or periodical could sell a single issue today if it restricted itself to the American language of twenty-eight years ago. It couldn't discuss half the things we are interested in, and its style would seem stiff and cumbrous. If the editorials were serious, the public—and the stockholders—have reason to be grateful that the writers on these publications are more literate than the editors.

And so back to our questions: what's a dictionary for, and how, in 1962, can it best do what it ought to do? The demands are simple. The common reader turns to a dictionary for information about the spelling, pronunciation, meaning, and proper use of words. He wants to know what is current and respectable. But he wants—and has a right to—the truth, the full truth. And the full truth about any language, and especially about American English today, is that there are many areas in which certainty is impossible and simplification is misleading.

Even in so settled a matter as spelling, a dictionary cannot always be absolute. *Theater* is correct, but so is *theatre*. And so are *traveled* and *travelled, plow* and *plough, catalog* and *catalogue,* and scores of other variants. The reader may want a single certainty. He may have taken an unyielding position in an argument, he may have wagered in support of his conviction and may demand that the dictionary "settle" the matter. But neither his vanity nor his purse is any concern of the dictionary's; it must record the facts. And the fact here is that there are many words in our language which may be spelled, with equal correctness, in either of two ways.

So with pronunciation. A citizen listening to his radio might notice that James B. Conant, Bernard Baruch, and Dwight D. Eisenhower pronounce *economics* as ECKuhnomiks, while A. Whitney Griswold, Adlai Stevenson, and Herbert Hoover pronounce it EEKuhnomiks. He turns to the dictionary to see which of the two pronunciations is "right" and finds that they are both acceptable.

Has he been betrayed? Has the dictionary abdicated its responsibility? Should it say that one *must* speak like the president of Harvard or like the president of Yale, like the thirty-first President of the United States or like the thirty-fourth? Surely it's none of its business to make a choice. Not because of the distinction of these particular speakers; lexicography, like God, is no respecter of persons. But because so widespread and conspicuous a use of two pronunciations among people of this elevation shows that there *are* two pronunciations. Their speaking establishes the fact which the dictionary must record.

Among the "enormities" with which *Life* taxes the Third International is its listing of "the common mispronunciation" *heighth*. That it is labeled a "dialectal variant" seems, somehow, to compound the felony. But one hears the word so pronounced, and if one professes to give a full account of American English in the 1960's, one has to take some cognizance of it. All people do not possess *Life*'s intuitive perception that the word is so "monstrous" that even to list it as a dialect variation is to merit scorn. Among these, by the way, was John Milton, who, in one of the greatest passages in all literature, besought the Holy Spirit to raise him to the "highth" of his great argument. And even the *Oxford English Dictionary* is so benighted as to list it, in full boldface, right alongside of *Height* as a variant that has been in the language since at least 1290.

Now there are still, apparently, millions of Americans who retain, in this as in much else, some of the speech of Milton. This particular pronunciation seems to be receding, but the *American Dialect Dictionary*[1] still records instances of it from almost every state on the Eastern seaboard and notes that it is heard from older people and "occasionally in educated speech," "common with good speakers," "general," "widespread."

Under these circumstances, what is a dictionary to do? Since millions speak the word this way, the pronunciation can't be ignored. Since it has been in use as long as we have any record of English and since it has been used by the greatest writers, it can't be described as substandard or slang. But it is heard now only in certain localities. That makes it a dialectal pronunciation, and an honest dictionary will list it as such. What else can it do? Should it do?

.   .   .

[1] Harold Wentworth, ed. (New York: Crowell, 1944).

The average purchaser of a dictionary uses it most often, probably, to find out what a word "means." As a reader, he wants to know what an author intended to convey. As a speaker or writer, he wants to know what a word will convey to his auditors. And this, too, is complex, subtle, and forever changing.

An illustration is furnished by an editorial in the Washington *Post* (January 17, 1962). After a ringing appeal to those who "love truth and accuracy" and the usual bombinations about "abdication of authority" and "barbarism," the editorial charges the Third International with "pretentious and obscure verbosity" and specifically instances its definition of "so simple an object as a door."

The definition reads:

a movable piece of firm material or a structure supported usu. along one side and swinging on pivots or hinges, sliding along a groove, rolling up and down, revolving as one of four leaves, or folding like an accordion by means of which an opening may be closed or kept open for passage into or out of a building, room, or other covered enclosure or a car, airplane, elevator, or other vehicle.

Then follows a series of special meanings, each particularly defined and, where necessary, illustrated by a quotation.

Since, aside from roaring and admonishing the "gentlemen from Springfield" that "accuracy and brevity are virtues," the *Post*'s editorial fails to explain what is wrong with the definition, we can only infer from "so simple" a thing that the writer takes the plain, downright, man-in-the-street attitude that a door is a door and any damn fool knows that.

But if so, he has walked into one of lexicography's biggest booby traps: the belief that the obvious is easy to define. Whereas the opposite is true. Anyone can give a fair description of the strange, the new, or the unique. It's the commonplace, the habitual, that challenges definition, for its very commonness compels us to define it in uncommon terms. Dr. Johnson was ridiculed on just this score when his dictionary appeared in 1755. For two hundred years his definition of a network as "any thing reticulated or decussated, at equal distances, with interstices between the intersections" has been good for a laugh. But in the merriment one thing is always overlooked: no one has yet come up with a better definition! Subsequent dictionaries defined it as a mesh and then defined a mesh as a network. That's simple, all right.

Anyone who attempts sincerely to state what the word *door* means in the United States of America today can't take refuge in a log cabin. There has been an enormous proliferation of closing and demarking devices and structures in the past twenty years, and anyone who tries to thread his way through the many meanings now included under *door* may have to sacrifice brevity to accuracy and even have to employ words that a limited vocabulary may find obscure.

Is the entrance to a tent a door, for instance? And what of the thing that seals the exit of an airplane? Is this a door? Or what of those sheets and jets of air that are now being used, in place of old-fashioned oak and hinges, to screen entrances and exits. Are they doors? And what of those accordion-like things that set off various sections of many modern apartments? The fine print in the lease takes it for granted that they are doors and that spaces demarked by them are rooms—and the rent is computed on the number of rooms.

Was I gypped by the landlord when he called the folding contraption that shuts off my kitchen a door? I go to the Second International, which the editor of the *Post* urges me to use in preference to the Third International. Here I find that a door is

The movable frame or barrier of boards, or other material, usually turning on hinges or pivots or sliding, by which an entranceway into a house or apartment is closed and opened; also, a similar part of a piece of furniture, as in a cabinet or bookcase.

This is only forty-six words, but though it includes the cellar door, it excludes the barn door and the accordion-like thing.

So I go to the Third International. I see at once that the new definition is longer. But I'm looking for accuracy, and if I must sacrifice brevity to get it, then I must. And, sure enough, in the definition which raised the *Post*'s blood pressure, I find the words "folding like an accordion." The thing *is* a door, and my landlord is using the word in one of its currently accepted meanings.

We don't turn to a work of reference merely for confirmation.

We all have words in our vocabularies which we have misunderstood, and to come on the true meaning of one of these words is quite a shock. All our complacency and self-esteem rise to oppose the discovery. But eventually we must accept the humiliation and laugh it off as best we can.

Some, often those who have set themselves up as authorities, stick to their error and charge the dictionary with being in a conspiracy against them. They are sure that their meaning is the only "right" one. And when the dictionary doesn't bear them out they complain about "permissive" attitudes instead of correcting their mistake.

The New York *Times* and the *Saturday Review* both regarded as contemptibly "permissive" the fact that one meaning of one word was illustrated by a quotation from Polly Adler. But a rudimentary knowledge of the development of any language would have told them that the underworld has been a far more active force in shaping and enriching speech than all the synods that have ever convened. Their attitude is like that of the patriot who canceled his subscription to the *Dictionary of American Biography* when he discovered that the very first volume included Benedict Arnold!

The ultimate of "permissiveness," singled out by almost every critic for special scorn, was the inclusion in the Third International of *finalize*. It was this, more than any other one thing, that was given as the reason for sticking to the good old Second International—that "peerless authority on American English," as the *Times* called it. But if it was such an authority, why didn't they look into it? They would have found *finalize* if they had.

And why shouldn't it be there? It exists. It's been recorded for two generations. Millions employ it every day. Two Presidents of the United States—men of widely differing cultural backgrounds—have used it in formal statements. And so has the Secretary-General of the United Nations, a man of unusual linguistic attainments. It isn't permitting the word but omitting it that would break faith with the reader. Because it is exactly the sort of word we want information about.

To list it as substandard would be to imply that it is used solely by the ignorant and the illiterate. But this would be a misrepresentation: President Kennedy and U Thant are highly educated men, and both are articulate and literate. It isn't even a freak form. On the contrary, it is a classic example of a regular process of development in English, a process which has given us such thoroughly accepted words as *generalize, minimize, formalize,* and *verbalize.* Nor can it be dismissed on logical grounds or on the ground that it is a mere duplication of *complete.* It says something that *complete* doesn't say and says it in a way that is significant in the modern bureaucratic world: one usually *completes* something which he has initiated but *finalizes* the work of others.

One is free to dislike the word. I don't like it. But the editor of a dictionary has to examine the evidence for a word's existence and seek it in context to get, as clearly and closely as he can, the exact meaning that it conveys to those who use it. And if it is widely used by well-educated, literate, reputable people, he must list it as a standard word. He is not compiling a volume of his own prejudices.

An individual's use of his native tongue is the surest index to his position within his community. And those who turn to a dictionary expect from it some statement of the current status of a word or a grammatical construction. And it is with the failure to assume this function that modern lexicography has been most fiercely charged. The charge is based on a naïve assumption that simple labels can be attached in all instances. But they can't. Some words are standard in some constructions and not in others. There may be as many shades of status as of meaning, and modern lexicography instead of abdicating this function has fulfilled it to a degree utterly unknown to earlier dictionaries.

Consider the word *fetch,* meaning to "go get and bring to." Until recently a standard word of full dignity ("Fetch me, I pray thee, a little water in a vessel"—I Kings 17:10), it has become slightly tainted. Perhaps the command latent in it is resented as undemocratic. Or maybe its use in training dogs to retrieve has made some people feel that it is an undignified word to apply to human beings. But, whatever the reason, there is a growing uncertainty about its status, and hence it is the sort of word that conscientious people look up in a dictionary.

Will they find it labeled "good" or "bad"? Neither, of course, because either applied indiscriminately would be untrue. The Third International lists nineteen different meanings of the verb *to fetch*. Of these some are labeled "dialectal," some "chiefly dialectal," some "obsolete," one "chiefly Scottish," and two "not in formal use." The primary meaning—"to go after and bring back" —is not labeled and hence can be accepted as standard, accepted with the more assurance because the many shades of labeling show us that the word's status has been carefully considered.

On grammatical questions the Third International tries to be equally exact and thorough. Sometimes a construction is listed without comment, meaning that in the opinion of the editors it is unquestionably respectable. Sometimes a construction carries the comment "used by speakers and writers on all educational levels though disapproved by some grammarians." Or the comment may be "used in substandard speech and formerly also by reputable writers." Or "less often in standard than in substandard speech." Or simply "dial."

And this very accurate reporting is based on evidence which is presented for our examination. One may feel that the evidence is inadequate or that the evaluation of it is erroneous. But surely, in the face of classification so much more elaborate and careful than any known heretofore, one cannot fly into a rage and insist that the dictionary is "out to destroy . . . every vestige of linguistic punctilio . . . every criterion for distinguishing between better usages and worse."

Words, as we have said, are continually shifting their meanings and connotations and hence their status. A word which has dignity, say, in the vocabulary of an older person may go down in other people's estimation. Like *fetch*. The older speaker is not likely to be aware of this and will probably be inclined to ascribe the snickers of the young at his speech to that degeneration of manners which every generation has deplored in its juniors. But a word which is coming up in the scale—like *jazz,* say, or, more recently, *crap*—will strike his ear at once. We are much more aware of offenses given us than of those we give. And if he turns to a dictionary and finds the offending word listed as standard—or even listed, apparently—his response is likely to be an outburst of indignation.

But the dictionary can neither snicker nor fulminate. It records. It will offend many, no doubt, to find the expression *wise up,* meaning to inform or to become informed, listed in the Third International with no restricting label. To my aging ears it still sounds like slang. But the evidence—quotations from the *Kiplinger Washington Letter* and the *Wall Street Journal*—convinces me that it is I who am out of step, lagging behind. If such publications have taken to using *wise up* in serious contexts, with no punctuational indication of irregularity, then it is obviously respectable. And finding it so listed and supported, I can only say that it's nice to be informed and sigh to realize that I am becoming an old fogy. But of course, I don't have to use it (and I'll be damned if I will! "Let them smile, as I do now, At the old forsaken bough Where I cling").

In part, the trouble is due to the fact that there is no standard for standard. Ideas of what is proper to use in serious, dignified speech and writing are changing—and with breathtaking rapidity. This is one of the major facts of contemporary American English. But it is no more the dictionary's business to oppose this process than to speed it up.

Even in our standard speech some words are more dignified and some more informal than others, and dictionaries have tried to guide us through these uncertainties by marking certain words and constructions as "colloquial," meaning "inappropriate in a formal situation." But this distinction, in the opinion of most scholars, has done more harm than good. It has created the notion that these particular words are inferior, when actually they might be the best possible words in an informal statement. And so—to the rage of many reviewers—the Third International has dropped this label. Not all labels, as angrily charged, but only this one out of a score. And the doing so may have been an error, but it certainly didn't constitute "betrayal" or "abandoning of all distinctions." It was intended to end a certain confusion.

In all the finer shades of meaning, of which the status of a word is only one, the user is on his own, whether he likes it or not.

Despite *Life*'s artless assumption about the Gettysburg Address, nothing worth writing is written *from* a dictionary. The dictionary, rather, comes along afterwards and describes what *has been* written.

Words in themselves are not dignified, or silly, or wise, or malicious. But they can be used in dignified, silly, wise, or malicious ways by dignified, silly, wise, or malicious people. *Egghead,* for example, is a perfectly legitimate word, as legitimate as *highbrow* or *long-haired.* But there is something very wrong and very undignified, by civilized standards, in a belligerent dislike for intelligence and education. *Yak* is an amusing word for persistent chatter. Anyone could say, "We were just yakking over a cup of coffee," with no harm to his dignity. But to call a Supreme Court decision *yakking* is to be vulgarly insulting and so, undignified. Again, there's nothing wrong with *confab* when it's appropriate. But when the work of a great research project, employing hundreds of distinguished scholars over several decades and involving the honor of one of the greatest publishing houses in the world, is described as *confabbing* (as the New York *Times* editorially described the preparation of the Third International), the use of this particular word asserts that the lexicographers had merely sat around and talked idly. And the statement becomes undignified— if not, indeed, slanderous.

The lack of dignity in such statements is not in the words, nor in the dictionaries that list them, but in the hostility that deliberately seeks this tone of expression. And in expressing itself the hostility frequently shows that those who are expressing it don't know how to use a dictionary. Most of the reviewers seem unable to read the Third International and unwilling to read the Second.

The *American Bar Association Journal,* for instance, in a typical outburst ("a deplorable abdication of responsibility"), picked out for special scorn the inclusion in the Third International of the word *irregardless.* "As far as the new Webster's is concerned," said the *Journal,* "this meaningless verbal bastard is just as legitimate as any other word in the dictionary." Thirty seconds spent in examining the book they were so roundly condemning would have shown them that in it *irregardless* is labeled "nonstand"—which means "nonstandard," which means "not conforming to the usage generally characteristic of educated native speakers of the language." Is that "just as legitimate as any other word in the dictionary"?

The most disturbing fact of all is that the editors of a dozen of the most influential publications in America today are under the impression that *authoritative* must mean *authoritarian*. Even the "permissive" Third International doesn't recognize this identification—editors' attitudes being not yet, fortunately, those of the American people. But the Fourth International may have to.

The new dictionary may have many faults. Nothing that tries to meet an ever-changing situation over a terrain as vast as contemporary English can hope to be free of them. And much in it is open to honest, and informed, disagreement. There can be linguistic objection to the eradication of proper names. The removal of guides to pronunciation from the foot of every page may not have been worth the valuable space it saved. The new method of defining words of many meanings has disadvantages as well as advantages. And of the half million or more definitions, hundreds, possibly thousands, may seem inadequate or imprecise. To some (of whom I am one) the omission of the label "colloquial" will seem meritorious; to others it will seem a loss.

But one thing is certain: anyone who solemnly announces in the year 1962 that he will be guided in matters of English usage by a dictionary published in 1934 is talking ignorant and pretentious nonsense.

APPLICATIONS

1. Turn to example I in this chapter, and read it again. Now rewrite it, substituting a specific word for every general word you find and a concrete word for every abstract one. Do not worry in the least if your version does not express what you think the writer intended. From the nature of the example, it is doubtful if he knew that either.

2. In the early days of our country, John Randolph was a fiery opponent of Henry Clay and also a master of invective. If Ran-

dolph had used "lightning-bug" words, he might have said of Clay, "He is a pretty bright man but not very honest." Make a serious effort to turn these lightning bugs into the kind of lightning Mark Twain had in mind.[11]

3. Take up the rewrite that you did for Application 1, Chapter 8. Without sacrificing economy of statement, change abstract words to concrete and general words to specific. Do you find any words that might carry unintended or undesirable connotations? Any words that do not seem quite right in the context as you see it now? Spend some time with *Roget's Thesaurus,* and see if you do not find at least a dozen words that you can change for the better.

[11] "So brilliant, yet so corrupt, which like the rotten mackerel by moonlight, shines and stinks."—JOHN RANDOLPH

10 | Final Polish

"What Counts Is the Job"—BERNARD DE VOTO

At long last you have down on paper a draft of your technical memorandum, report of an investigation, paper for publication in a professional journal, or perhaps a chapter for your projected book. You may have dashed it off as fast as you could type, in a fine frenzy of inspiration, or you may have trudged through a longhand scroll, weighing every word before you set it down. In either case this first draft may not be fit to be read by anyone but yourself.

The worst thing you can do at this point is to start worrying about it. *Don't.* There is no need to. If you have followed all of the design steps set forth in the preceding chapters, your presentation will be structurally sound. The essential parts will be there, and they will perform their intended functions. You have assembled them by proven methods, and you have built a machine that will serve the purpose you designed it for.

Consider briefly all the thought and effort you have given to this first draft that you now have before you.

- You have carefully appraised your reader and how to reach him most effectively, both in terms of modern communication theory and from practical considerations of what reading level he can most readily grasp.
- You have defined your purpose by reviewing all the facts your reader needs to know; by organizing your material in logical sequence; and by structuring your paragraphs for unity, coherence, and emphasis.
- You have thought long about your subject and determined to your own satisfaction exactly what you want to say about it. Your sentences emphasize important ideas and subordinate those less important. You have avoided many common sentence errors that hinder the reader. You have breathed life into your work, and at every opportunity you have used concrete and specific words rather than abstract and general ones.

In short, you have built a machine that runs. What remains is a polish job: *revision*. Some writers rather enjoy revision—others loathe it—but no one has ever found a way around it. It is harder to dodge than the tax man. Having once faced this, the sensible strategy is to devise the most efficient plan—for you—of getting the job done.

Many writers have set down their own observations of what works best for them, and we find a range of rubrics of revision. Common to all is the writer's conscious effort to put himself into the mind of a reader who has never seen the work. Of course this ideal can never be fully met, but it can be approached. The simplest method is to put the first draft aside for a while. Forget it completely. Do something entirely different: chop wood; read; play bridge; go to a concert; or throw a party. Afterward, take up the first draft again, and try to see it from the viewpoint of a reader who has no notion whatever of what you want to tell him.

Some writers call this the "fallowing" process, and it is an apt term. While you were occupying yourself with something different, your subconscious mind was continually at work—clarifying concepts, choosing better wording, rearranging organization, and in general pulling the whole picture together so that it makes unified sense.

How long should you let a piece of work lie fallow? Only you can answer this. It depends both on your own temperament and on the demands that others make on you. If you are a college undergraduate and you delay writing a term paper so that it takes you until 3 A.M. to draft a paper due at 8 A.M., your fallowing time will approach zero, and you will probably deserve the grade you get. Overnight fallowing is a fair compromise, and many writers find this adequate. Others prefer to let their first drafts lie for at least a week.

If you are a professional engineer or scientist in industry, the time you can allow will obviously depend on your job. If you are preparing a paper for publication in a professional journal and have no set deadline, you can proceed at your own pace. But if your boss tells you at noon Thursday that he must have a report by Friday at five so he can catch a New York plane, then you do your best in the time you have.

Closely related to fallowing is the problem of *how many* revisions to make. This too is subject to variation and will depend on time demands and the quality of work you aspire to. As a guide to a norm, let us look at some typical practices of professional writers.

Some writers can develop a satisfactory piece with one revision. This means that they find satisfactory answers to all the questions [aimed at discovering their own imperfections] at one rewriting. Because of the number of [these] questions few writers seem to be able to do this all at once. Hence there usually is a third, a fourth, and even further drafts. The number seems to depend on the writer and his habits of work. The English historian G. M. Trevelyan usually found four drafts necessary. The Pulitzer prize winner Conrad Richter often prepares as many as ten drafts. Perhaps three or four is the average. Margery Allingham made the following statement: "I write every paragraph four times—once to get my meaning down, once to put in anything I have left out, once to take out anything that seems unnecessary, and once to make the whole thing sound as if I had only just thought of it."[1]

You will note that these are practices of professional writers. As an engineer or scientist whose main job is technical, you will be writing because your job demands it, and you may reach a point of diminishing returns before you have reached ten drafts or even four. In his own industrial experience the present author had two sharply contrasting assignments that illustrate the different amounts of revision that different jobs may justify.

The first concerned a rather short report—no more than 10,000 words—on the results of a survey of direct interest to the president of the company. It would be superfluous to say that this author wished to turn out the best report of which he was capable. The number of drafts *exceeded* ten, and since other daily duties would not wait, the time consumed amounted to most evenings throughout a long summer. From a practical standpoint, was it worth it? This author thought so—upon receiving a bonus check in four figures.

The second report was a labor relations history of one company covering a period of nearly ten years. The finished report was demanded within a week. By dictating steadily for fourteen to sixteen hours a day, this writer finished a first draft of some 60,000 words in five days. You will not be surprised to learn that the revisions on that draft were few and sketchy and that the result would have taken no prize in composition. But the job got done. If time had allowed, a far better presentation could have been made; at a guess, it might have run to 25,000 words, rather than 60,000, and the readers would have been saved much valuable time. But there it was. As the French novelist remarked upon closing a letter to a friend: "I'm sorry this letter has been so long—I didn't have time to write a short one."

At the opposite end of the spectrum is the writing you will want to do to enhance your professional status. Let us suppose that you wish to prepare an important paper for a professional journal or perhaps a chapter for a book. Suppose further that you

[1] Paul R. Reynolds, *The Writing and Selling of Non-Fiction* (Garden City, N.Y.: Doubleday, 1963), p. 31.

have done the best job that you know how: getting down what you want to say; putting in the things you forgot to say; taking out the things that did not belong; and finally smoothing the whole thing out so that when you read it aloud, it flowed along smoothly enough to please you.

You heave a sigh of relief and send it off to the publisher.

What happens then?

What happens then is that a copy editor goes to work on your manuscript—and for this you can be grateful. The suggestions that a copy editor can make for the improvement of your own "best" product will be invaluable. William Bridgwater, editor in chief of the Columbia University Press and advisory editor of the Dryden Press, has explained this little-known process from a background of long experience. Here are some of the points he makes about the copy editor's job:

Take the manuscript of a book. Set it firmly upon a desk or table so that it cannot slip or slide. Pick up a pencil. Start reading through the manuscript, and as you read correct typographical errors and note passages that may confuse a reader and usages that may cause trouble for a printer. You are doing copy editing.

If the job sounds easy, you do not understand it. There are many complications, not the least of them being that it is a task without thoroughly set limits. . . .

Usually the copy editor is handed a manuscript. It is given to him by the publisher, the general editor, the author, or some other agent, with the assurance that there are practically no flaws in it (even if the author is an Eskimo who has just learned to read and write) and almost always with the admonition that it must be edited immediately and in great haste because of the publication schedule. . . .

The fundamental. unavoidable, and not infrequently boring part of copy editing is the discovery in the manuscript of all usages that may hinder the reader or may stop him short and make him leave the book altogether, like a man dragging his feet out of a swamp. And "usages" include not only misspelled words and missing or excessive punctuation, but also more important items, such as meaningless headings and references to nonexistent illustrations. These hindrances the copy editor must find and remove by exercise of his pencil. . . .[2]

2 Gerald Gross, *Editors on Editing* (New York: Universal Library, 1962), pp. 52, 53, 56.

By the time your manuscript comes back from such a conscientious copy editor, your patience may have worn thin. It may wear even thinner when you see the amount of work he has done "by exercise of his pencil." Perhaps this would be a good time to go to the gym for a fast round with the punching bag. When you come back to your desk, freshly showered and with an open mind, compare your original with the revisions your copy editor has made. No book—no educational institution anywhere—can teach you more about rewriting than the pages that now lie before you. If you fully apprehend the reasons that underlie your editor's suggestions, you should have it made.

The Principles of Poor Writing

Paul W. Merrill

The late Dr. Paul W. Merrill received his A.B. from Stanford University in 1908 and his Ph.D. in astronomy from the University of California in 1913. He was an astronomer at Lick Observatory, an instructor in astronomy at the University of Michigan, a physicist with the National Bureau of Standards, and from 1919 to 1952, an astronomer at the Mount Wilson and Palomar observatories in Pasadena. An authority on wave lengths of spectrum lines, photography in the red and infrared, and stellar spectroscopy, he was awarded the Bruce Medal of the Astronomical Society of the Pacific in 1946, and the Draper Medal of the National Academy of Sciences that same year. For twelve years, he served as editor of Mount Wilson astronomical publications.

BOOKS AND ARTICLES ON GOOD WRITING ARE NUMEROUS, BUT where can you find sound, practical advice on how to write poorly? Poor writing is so common that every educated person ought to know something about it. Many scientists actually do write poorly, but they probably perform by ear without perceiving clearly how their results are achieved. An article on the principles of poor writing might help. The author considers himself well qualified to prepare such an article; he can write poorly without half trying.

The average student finds it surprisingly easy to acquire

Reprinted from *Scientific Monthly*, LXIV (January, 1947), 72–74. By permission of the American Association for the Advancement of Science and Mrs. Ruth C. Merrill.

the usual tricks of poor writing. To do a consistently poor job, however, one must grasp a few essential principles:

I. Ignore the reader.
II. Be verbose, vague, and pompous.
III. Do not revise.

Ignore the Reader

The world is divided into two great camps: yourself and others. A little obscurity or indirection in writing will keep the others at a safe distance; if they get close, they may see too much.

Write as if for a diary. Keep your mind on a direct course between yourself and the subject; don't think of the reader—he makes a bad triangle. This is fundamental. Constant and alert consideration of the probable reaction of the reader is a serious menace to poor writing; moreover, it requires mental effort. A logical argument is that if you write poorly enough, your readers will be too few to merit any attention whatever.

Ignore the reader wherever possible. If the proposed title, for example, means something to you, stop right there; think no further. If the title baffles or misleads the reader, you have won the first round. Similarly, all the way through you must write for yourself, not for the reader. Practice a dead-pan technique, keeping your facts and ideas all on the same level of emphasis with no telltale hints of relative importance or logical sequence. Use long sentences containing many ideas loosely strung together. *And* is the connective most frequently employed in poor writing because it does not indicate cause and effect, nor does it distinguish major ideas from subordinate ones. *Because* seldom appears in poor writing, nor does the semicolon—both are replaced by *and*.

Camouflage transitions in thought. Avoid such connectives as *moreover, nevertheless, on the other hand.* If unable to resist the temptation to give some signal for a change in thought, use *however.* A poor sentence may well begin with *however,* because to the reader, with no idea of what comes next, *however* is too vague to be useful. A good sentence begins with the subject or with a phrase that needs emphasis.

The "hidden antecedent" is a common trick of poor writing. Use a pronoun to refer to a noun a long way back, or to one decidedly subordinate in thought or syntax; or the pronoun may refer to something not directly expressed. If you wish to play a little game with the reader, offer him the wrong antecedent as bait; you may be astonished how easy it is to catch the poor fish.

In ignoring the reader avoid parallel constructions which give the thought away too easily. I need not elaborate, for you probably employ inversion frequently. It must have been a naive soul who said, "When the thought is parallel, let the phrases be parallel."

In every technical paper omit a few items that most readers need to know. You had to discover these things the hard way; why make it easy for the reader? Avoid defining symbols; never specify the units in which data are presented. Of course it will be beneath your dignity to give numerical values of constants in formulae. With these omissions, some papers may be too short; lengthen them by explaining things that do not need explaining. In describing tables, give special attention to self-explanatory headings; let the reader hunt for the meaning of P^1r_0.

Be Verbose, Vague, and Pompous

The cardinal sin of poor writing is to be concise and simple. Avoid being specific; it ties you down. Use plenty of deadwood: include many superfluous words and phrases. Wishful thinking suggests to a writer that verbosity somehow serves as a cloak or even as a mystic halo by which an idea may be glorified. A cloud of words may conceal defects in observation or analysis, either by opacity or by diverting the reader's attention. Introduce abstract nouns at the drop of a hat—even in those *cases* where the *magnitude* of the *motion* in a downward *direction* is inconsiderable. Make frequent use of the words *case, character, condition, former* and *latter, nature, such, very.*

Poor writing, like good football, is strong on razzle-dazzle, weak on information. Adjectives are frequently used to bewilder the reader. It isn't much trouble to make them gaudy or hyperbolic; at least they can be flowery and inexact.

DEADWOOD

Bible: Render to Caesar the things that are Caesar's.

Poor: In the case of Caesar it might well be considered appropriate from a moral or ethical point of view to render to that potentate all of those goods and materials of whatever character or quality which can be shown to have had their original source in any portion of the domain of the latter.

Shakespeare: I am no orator as Brutus is.

Poor: The speaker is not what might be termed an adept in the profession of public speaking, as might be properly stated of Mr. Brutus.

Concise: The dates of several observations are in doubt.

Poor: It should be mentioned that in the case of several observations there is room for considerable doubt concerning the correctness of the dates on which they were made.

Reasonable: Exceptionally rapid changes occur in the spectrum.

Poor: There occur in the spectrum changes which are quite exceptional in respect to the rapidity of their advent.

Reasonable: Formidable difficulties, both mathematical and observational, stand in the way.

Poor: There are formidable difficulties of both a mathematical and an observational nature that stand in the way.

Reasonable: Two sunspots changed rapidly.

Poor: There are two cases where sunspots changed with considerable rapidity.

Reasonable: Three stars are red.

Poor: In three cases the stars are red in color.

RAZZLE-DAZZLE

- Immaculate precision of observation and extremely delicate calculations . . .
- It would prove at once a world imponderable, etherealized. Our actions would grow grandific.
- Well for us that the pulsing energy of the great life-giving dynamo in the sky never ceases. Well, too, that we are at a safe distance from the flame-licked whirlpools into which our earth might drop like a pellet of waste fluff shaken into the live coals of a grate fire.

Do Not Revise

Write hurriedly, preferably when tired. Have no plan; write down items as they occur to you. The article will thus be spontaneous and poor. Hand in your manuscript the moment it is finished. Rereading a few days later might lead to revision—which seldom, if ever, makes the writing worse. If you submit your manuscript to colleagues (a bad practice), pay no attention to their criticisms or comments. Later resist firmly any editorial suggestions. Be strong and infallible; don't let anyone break down your personality. The critic may be trying to help you or he may have an ulterior motive, but the chance of his causing improvement in your writing is so great that you must be on guard.

Pieces
for Analysis

The following pieces are presented for your analysis along the lines suggested in the text. Each has a degree of professional finish, but none is offered as a perfect model of its type, and none would be harmed by further polish. You will benefit most from your study if you will make your own close analysis of these pieces, and write out your own specific and detailed conclusions on how they could be improved.

A. A Technical Abstract

Readability of Technical Writing

Ritchie R. Ward

THE APPLICABILITY OF SEVEN PUBLISHED READABILITY FOR-
mulas for estimating the communicative effectiveness of scientific and engineering writing has been studied. The formula
scores were compared with the independent judgments of a
panel of 96 senior scientists and engineers on the relative
effectiveness of 20 examples of published technical writing.
Quite good correlations were found between the panel judgments and most of the readability formula scores, the panel
rating "best" those examples that the formulas classified as
most readable, and conversely. The judges were in good

From *Proceedings, 14th International Communications Conference,* Society of Technical Writers and Publishers, Chicago (May, 1967), p. 32.

agreement in their evaluations of the examples which they rated either "very good" or "very poor," while in the intermediate range, their opinions were more variable. Overall, agreement appeared to be close enough to justify reasonable confidence in the consensus.

Of the seven readability formulas studied, the Gunning Fog Index appears on balance to be the most practicable for general use by professional technical men. If a writer finds samples of his work scoring much above a Fog Index level of 15, he can be reasonably sure that his colleagues (especially those in other disciplines) will regard his writing as fair to very poor.

While no readability formula can ensure a good style, the use of a suitable one can "help eliminate guessing at clarity of statement, and provide a useful measuring device. In short, it can help a writer see his material as a reader will."

B. A Book Chapter

What Is Language?

Archibald A. Hill

*Archibald A. Hill received his A.B. from Pomona College, his
M.A. from Stanford University, and his Ph.D. from Yale Uni-
versity in 1927. He has taught English at the University of Michi-
gan and English philology at the University of Virginia. At
Georgetown University, he was vice-director of the Institute of
Language and Linguistics. Dr. Hill has been professor of English
at the University of Texas since 1955. He is a member of the
Modern Language Association and secretary of the Linguistic
Society of America.*

1. Some Basic Assumptions

The subject of linguistics presents an initial difficulty because
the word which designates it is unfamiliar. The word can
easily be defined as the scientific analysis of language, but it
is doubtful if such a definition is meaningful to anyone who
lacks familiarity with this kind of analytic activity. It is far
better to begin by defining language, since language is closer
to the reader's experience. Yet even the definition of language
presents unsuspected difficulties and needs preliminary discussion before it is attempted directly.

   If a group of educated speakers are asked to define the

From *Introduction to Linguistic Structures* by Archibald A. Hill, © 1958
by Harcourt, Brace & World, Inc. and reprinted with their permission.

language they are using, the reply will probably be "All the words and sentences used to express our thoughts." The definition is satisfactory in everyday situations, since long practice has made plain what is meant, and consequently most hearers know how to respond accurately. But for all that, the definition is not sufficiently accurate to be the basis for analysis. Terms like "words and sentences," which seem transparent to a speaker of a Western language, would be more misleading than enlightening if applied to some languages. Moreover, there are phenomena similar to language which this definition does not identify. Most important, the definition identifies language activity by thought. Language activity can be observed, and is therefore subject to verification. Thought can be observed only by subjective introspection, and so is not subject to verification. Language activity is therefore more knowable, thought less knowable. Obviously a definition must define the less knowable by the more knowable if it is to cast light. In what follows, such a definition will be attempted. There must first be a warning, the need for which will be clearer as we advance. A definition is not a description. A definition gives only those characteristics which have diagnostic value for recognition. A description attempts to give all characteristics, preferably in the order of their importance. A definition necessarily leaves out much and may make use of relatively trivial characteristics, but it is not to be condemned for that reason.

Most professional students of language proceed from a few assumptions, one of which is that the fundamental forms of language activity are the sequences of sounds made by human lips, tongues, and vocal cords—the phenomena usually distinguished by the narrower name of "speech." Though this first assumption may seem like a truism, it is important, since many who accept it verbally still act as if they did not believe it. Some few even deny it. There are only two reasons for questioning the assumption. Writing has great permanence and great prestige. Further, the basis of our education is training in the manipulation of written symbols of ever-increasing complexity. Highly literate people, and those who would like to be literate, are therefore apt to think of writing as the real center of language and of speech as peripheral and derived—often badly—from the written forms.

There are a number of facts which should settle this question of priority. First, speech reaches back to the origins of human society; writing has a history of only about seven thousand years.[1] Also, no contemporary community of men is without language, even though it is probably still true that most of the world's several thousand language communities remain in the preliterate stage, without benefit of alphabet or even picture symbol. Individual members of literate communities, furthermore, learn their language some years before they learn to read or write it; and adults, even adults who are professional writers, carry on a good deal more speech activity in daily living than activity involving writing. The final fact is that all writing systems are essentially representations of the forms of speech, rather than representations of ideas or objects in the nonlinguistic world. There are exceptions to this statement, like the Arabic numbers which work independently of the words for numbers in the Western languages. The exceptions, however, are in a minority disproportionate to the majority of symbols which always indicate the forms of language. The point can be driven home by a pair of simple examples. The symbol for *one* in Japanese writing is a single stroke, that for *two* two strokes, and so on. It might be thought that such a symbol has no relation to the Japanese word for *one* (*ichi*) but represents instead the nonlinguistic idea of "oneness." Actually the occurrence of the single stroke is correlated with the occurrence of the word. It occurs not only in the number but also in such forms as *ichiji, primary*. The Japanese symbol, therefore, has a quite different range from

[1] The great antiquity of language, as compared with writing, is a reasonable assumption, but it is often presented without evidence. To arrive at the conclusion that language is older than writing, linguists and anthropologists start from the observed fact that in modern communities, all organized cooperative activity rests firmly and necessarily on language as the means of controlling and directing interaction. This being so in all observed communities, it is assumed by archaeological anthropologists that when remains of past communities show material evidence of social organization, these remains are those of communities which possessed language. Communities which show such evidences of social organization also show artifacts or other evidences which are much older than the remains of any communities which show evidences of even primitive systems of writing. It is possible that early human communities possessed some other form of highly organized communication, such as the gesture language which has been occasionally proposed since the days of Locke (cf. Max Müller, *Lectures on the Science of Language*, London, 1862, p. 31). But though possible, such a nonvocal symbol system is unlikely. Language is now a universal activity; it is an extra and unnecessary hypothesis to suppose something else.

the letter sequence *one* of English, which is not used in the dissimilar word *primary*. The one-stroke symbol corresponds with the occurrence of the Japanese word *ichi,* proving that the one-stroke symbol is a representation of the word (though an understandably pictorial one), and not a direct representation of the idea of oneness.

Written symbols can be understood, furthermore, insofar as they fit into a linguistic structure, even when they refer to nothing in the nonlinguistic world. Thus, if an English text should have the sentence, "He *sprashes* it," the second word could immediately be recognized as a verb in the third person singular and as a sequence of sounds quite in accord with English structural habits, though it represents nothing in the outside world at all. For the purposes of this book, therefore, the linguist's assumption that language is a set of sounds will be adopted. It is no contradiction of this assumption that the sounds can be secondarily translated into visual marks, grooves on a wax disc, electrical impulses, or finger movements.

Linguists assume that the description and analysis of language must begin with description of the sounds and their patterning and that description of meaning must be put off until the first task is done. Such an attitude is often misunderstood to be a denial of meaning, but this is not true. The linguist's desire to put off analysis of meaning is no more than an application of the principle of working from the more knowable to the less knowable, and though linguistics has not as yet had very striking results in semantic analysis, it can be hoped that the next few decades will see results of real value in semantics.

2. The Defining Characteristics of Language

Working with the assumptions given above, linguists can offer a set of five defining characteristics which serve to set off language from other forms of symbolic behavior and to establish language as a purely human activity. Often animal communication will have one or more of these five characteristics, but never all of them.

First, language, as has been said, is a set of sounds. This is perhaps the least important characteristic, since the communication of mammals and birds is also a set of sounds. On the other hand, the system of communication which is in some ways most strikingly like language, that of bees, is a set of body movements, not sounds. It would be easy, further, to imagine a language based on something else than sound, but no human language is so constructed. Even the manual language of the deaf is derived from the preexistent spoken language of the community.

Second, the connection between the sounds, or sequences of sounds, and objects of the outside world is arbitrary and unpredictable. That is to say, a visitor from Mars would be unable to predict that in London a given animal is connected with the sound sequence written *dog,* in Paris with the sequence *chien,* in Madrid with *perro.* The arbitrary quality of language symbols is not infrequently denied, for a number of reasons. Sometimes the denial is based on nothing more than the notion that the forms of one's native language are so inevitably right that they must be instinctive for all proper men. Sometimes the denial is more subtle. It is often maintained that all language, even though now largely arbitrary, must once have been a systematic imitation of objects by means of sound. It is true that there are some imitative words in all languages, but they are at best a limited part of the vocabulary. It is easy to imitate the noise of a barking dog, for instance, but difficult if not impossible to imitate a noiseless object, such as a rainbow. Though imitative words show similarity in many languages, absolute identity is rare. A dog goes "bow-wow" in English, but in related languages he often goes "wow-wow" or "bow-bow." The imitative words do not, after all, entirely escape from the general arbitrariness of language. The imitative origin of language appears, therefore, at worst unlikely and at best unprovable. The same injunction holds for theories of language origin which speculate that it is an imitation of facial or other gestures.

If it is assumed that language is arbitrary, what is meant by the statement? Just that the sounds of speech and their connection with entities of experience are passed on to all members of any community by older members of that community. Therefore, a human being cut off from contact with a speech community can never learn to talk as that community does, and cut off from all speech communities never learns to talk at all. In essence, to say that language is arbitrary is merely to say that it is social. This is perhaps the most important thing that can be said about language.

In contrast, much of animal communication is instinctive rather than social. That is to say, all cats mew and purr, and would do so even if they were cut off from all communication with other cats. On the other hand, some animal communication seems to share the social nature of human speech and is therefore a learned activity. A striking example is the barking of dogs, which is characteristic only of the domesticated animal, not of dogs in the wild state. Similarly, the honey dances of bees may not be altogether without an arbitrary element. It is also likely that when more is known of the cries and chatterings of the great apes in the wild state, a considerable social element in their communication may be found. Nor should it be thought that all human communication is social. A part of our communication consists of instinctive reactions which accompany language, like the trembling of fear or the suffusion of blood which accompanies anger. Yet even in the nonlinguistic accompaniments of speech, the tones of voice and the gestures, it is now clear that there is more of arbitrary and socially learned behavior than had at one time been supposed.

Third, language is systematic. I cannot hope to make this statement completely clear at this point, since the whole of this book is devoted to the exposition of the system of language. However, some observations may now be made about the system of language. As in any system, language entities are arranged in recurrent designs, so that if a part of the design is seen, predictions can be made about the whole of it, as a triangle can be drawn if one side and two angles are given. Suppose there is an incomplete sentence like "John ——s Mary an ——." A good deal about what must fill the two blanks is obvious. The first must be a verb, the second a noun. Furthermore, not all verbs will go in the first blank, since it requires a verb whose third person singular is spelled with -s and which can take two objects (that is, not such a verb as *look* or *see*). Nor will all nouns fit in the second place, since an initial vowel is required, and the noun must be one which takes an article. There is no difficulty in deciding that the sentence could be either "John gives Mary an apple" or "John hands Mary an aspirin," but not "John *gaves* Mary an *book.*"[2]

Another observation that can be made about language systems is that every occurrence of language is a substitution frame. Any sentence is a series of entities, for each of which a whole group of other entities can be substituted without changing the frame. Thus the sentence "John gives Mary an apple" is such a substitution frame. For *John* there can be replacements like *he, Jack, William, the man, her husband,* or many others. For the verb, entities like *buys, takes, offers,* as well as the alternatives *hands* or *gives,* may be used. This characteristic of extensive substitutability for all parts of any language utterance is of some importance in that it enables us to say that parrots, no matter how startlingly human their utterances may be, are not carrying on language activity. A parakeet may produce the sentence "Birds can't talk!" with human pitch, voice tones, and nearly perfect sounds. But the bird never says "Dogs can't talk!" or "Birds can't write!" His utterance is a unit, not a multiple substitution frame.

Still another characteristic of language systems is that the entities of language are grouped into classes, always simpler, more predictable, and more sharply separated than the infinite variety of objects in the world. For instance, a whole series of objects is grouped under the single word *chair,* and *chair* is put into the large class of nouns. In dealing with objects in the outside world it may be difficult to decide whether something is a chair, a stool, or merely a rock. In language, we think of nouns and verbs as quite separate and are apt to say that the one class represents things, the other events. But in the outside world, as the physicists tell us, it is often hard to decide whether an object is best described as a thing or as an event.

To return once more to the defining characteristics of language, the fourth characteristic is that it is a set of symbols. That is

[2] In this book, an asterisk placed before a form means that it is believed to be impossible. In historical treatments of language, on the other hand, an asterisk before a form indicates that it has been reconstructed by comparison but is not actually recorded. These two uses of the asterisk should not be confused.

to say, language has meaning. In this form the statement is a platitude and does not distinguish language from other activities which are also symbolic. The nature of language symbols turns out to be rather different from the symbols of other types of communication. The simplest nonlinguistic symbol can be defined as a substitute stimulus. Pavlov's famous dogs, fed at the sound of a bell, eventually began to drool at the sound of the bell even when no food was present. The dogs were responding to a substitute stimulus. Nonlinguistic symbols can also be substitute responses, and these can also be taught to animals. A dog who learns to "speak" at the sight of food has learned such a substitute response. In human speech, however, one of the most striking facts is that we can talk about things which are not present, and we can talk about things which ordinarily produce a strong physical reaction without experiencing that reaction. For instance, I can talk about apples even though there are none in the room, and I can talk about them without always making my mouth water, even when I am hungry. This type of language, which occurs without an immediately present stimulus or response, is called "displaced speech," and is obviously of great importance. It is what enables man to know something of the past and of the world beyond the limited range of his vision and hearing at a given moment.

The crucial fact in producing this almost miraculous and purely human effect seems to be that a given language entity can be both substitute stimulus and substitute response, and can also be a stimulus for further language responses or response to other language stimuli. I can talk about apples when they are absent because "something reminds me of them." That is, I can make language responses to what is before me, and these language responses can stimulate the further response *apple* without any direct physical stimulus to my vision, touch, or smell. *Apple* can call forth still further language entities, like *pear* or *banana,* in an endless chain; these entities are also both stimuli and responses. When human speakers do this, they are setting up what philosophers call a "universe of discourse." The ability to make connected discourse within the symbol system is what enables men to talk at length, and profitably, about things they have never seen. By means of language men make elaborate models of distant experience and eventually test their accuracy by acting upon them. All that is known of animal communication leads to the supposition that precisely what is absent from it is the kind of symbolic activity here described, symbolic activity connected not merely with experience but with all parts of the symbol system itself. We believe, in short, that animals are incapable of displaced speech.

The paragraphs above are rather general, so that a concrete example may be helpful. Let us suppose that two speakers of English are together in a room. One of them is cold. A direct response for him would be to close the window.

Instead of this he can use the substitute response, which is also substitute stimulus: "John, please close the window for me." John can either close the window or reply with a further substitute: "Just a minute. Wait until I finish this page." Such a reply may produce acceptance or may lead to a discussion of John's procrastinating character, of the fact that his parents did not discipline him properly in youth, and that modern young people are generally rebellious and unmannerly. To all of this John may reply that modern times are marked by progress and the disappearance of old taboos. In the meantime the window may have been quietly closed, or completely forgotten in the warmth of discussion. What is important is that each speaker has begun reacting, not to the immediate situation, but to the other's language and his own. And in so doing, each has been building a model of general social conditions, of wide scope and ultimately of some value, even in a random and unchecked conversation of the sort described.

We are now ready to turn to the last defining characteristic of language, the fact that it is complete. By this is meant that whenever a human language has been accurately observed, it has been found to be so elaborated that its speakers can make a linguistic response to any experience they may undergo. This complex elaboration is such a regular characteristic of all languages, even those of the simplest societies, that linguists have long ago accepted it as a universal characteristic. Nevertheless, in early books about language, and in the descriptions by linguistically untrained travelers today, there are statements that tribe X has a language with only two or three hundred words in it, forcing the tribe to eke out its vocabulary by gesture.[3] Linguists maintain that all such statements are the product of lack of knowledge, and are false. Skepticism about such statements is borne out by the fact that in all instances where it was possible to check on tribe X, its language proved to be as complete as usual, whereupon the statement was transferred to tribe Y, whose language was as yet unknown. The statement that human language is complete once again serves to distinguish it from animal activity. In the communication of bees, for instance, the subjects of systematic discourse are severely limited. Bees cannot, apparently, make an utterance equivalent to "The beekeeper is coming."

The statement that human language is always complete should not be interpreted to mean that every language has a word for everything. Obviously the ancient Greeks had no words for automobiles or atom bombs, and probably the modern Yahgan of Tierra del Fuego lack them as well. The completeness of language lies rather in the fact that a speaker of ancient Greek would have been perfectly capable of describing an automobile had he seen one, and further that had automobiles become important in ancient Greece, the speakers of Greek would have been perfectly capable of coining a word for them. It is a characteristic of vocabulary that, except in languages which have gone out of use, it is always expansible, in spite of the fact that resistance to new forms may frequently appear. Since language enables the user to make appropriate responses to all things and since vocabulary is thus characteristically "open," differences in vocabulary between two languages are not an accurate measure of the difference in efficiency or excellence of the two tongues. The fact that Eskimo does not

[3] A typical recent statement of this sort was reported by Leonard Bloomfield in "Secondary and Tertiary Responses to Language," *Language*, XX, 1944, p. 49n.

"A physician, of good general background and education, who had been hunting in the north woods, told me that the Chippewa language contains only a few hundred words. Upon question, he said that he got this information from his guide, a Chippewa Indian. When I tried to state the diagnostic setting, the physician, our host, briefly and with signs of displeasure repeated his statement and turned his back to me. A third person, observing this discourtesy, explained that I had some experience of the language in question. This information had no effect."

For a good general account of the completeness of primitive languages and the use of gesture as a substitute among mutually unintelligible language groups, consult Ralph L. Beals and Harry Hoijer, *An Introduction to Anthropology*, Macmillan, New York, 1956, pp. 508–511.

have as highly developed a vocabulary of philosophy as does German merely indicates that the Eskimos are less interested in philosophy; on the other hand, Eskimo has a highly developed vocabulary for various kinds of snow, indicating that snow is important in Eskimo society. The completeness of human language and the openness of vocabulary make a groundless chimera of the occasionally expressed fear that a language might so degenerate as to become useless.

We can now attempt a definition of language, though the definition will be cumbersome. Language is the primary and most highly elaborated form of human symbolic activity. Its symbols are made up of sounds produced by the vocal apparatus, and they are arranged in classes and patterns which make up a complex and symmetrical structure. The entities of language are symbols, that is, they have meaning, but the connection between symbol and thing is arbitrary and socially controlled. The symbols of language are simultaneously substitute stimuli and substitute responses and can call forth further stimuli and responses, so that discourse becomes independent of an immediate physical stimulus. The entities and structure of language are always so elaborated as to give the speaker the possibility of making a linguistic response to any experience. Most of the above can be paraphrased by saying that every language is a model of a culture and its adjustment to the world.

3. Language and the Study of Its Nature

Since language is something that we habitually take for granted, it may not be clear, even after this discussion, why language and, even more, the study of language are important. Primarily they are important because language is a solely human activity, which separates man from other living beings. But though this may be readily granted, it is not always realized how fundamentally language is a defining characteristic of man. Even among students of man it is probably more common to define him as the "tool-making animal" than as the "talking animal." But it is quite possible that tool making is less crucially human than talking is. For one thing, it is natural that an archaeologist's attention should turn toward tools, which can be dug up, rather than toward language, which cannot. For another, it is not always easy to recognize how fundamental language is, even in our own society. There are individuals who lead nearly normal lives in spite of being deprived of speech, so that it may be argued that speech—admittedly the fundamental form of language—is a dispensable form of activity. Yet such speechless individuals always develop some form of substitute language, and all such substitutes presuppose the individual's membership in a society fully provided with speech. There are many things, such as wearing neckties, making movies, or cooking, which only human beings do. But many of these are not universal among men, and all of them are secondary. As for tool making, this activity is universally human, but it is in some sense shared with the higher primates. When, however, it is argued that tool making involves more than the use of a convenient stick or stone and is the purposeful molding of an object for future use, it would seem that the tool maker is an individual capable of displaced speech and of shaping his activity in accord with a symbolic model. In other words, as soon as man is defined as a maker of tools whose use lies in the future, we presuppose the existence of language. Therefore linguists, and many anthropologists, believe that language is the phenomenon most basic in human society. Historical anthropologists assume that when humanoid remains are found in a situation indicating an organized community, they are necessarily remains of a group possessed of language. If, then, it is language more than anything else we can observe which makes us men, it is ultimately the study of language which is most likely to throw light on the essential humanness of human beings. I wish at this point, however, to make a specific disclaimer. There are characteristics inaccessible to science which also distinguish man; the science of language is not concerned with these and should under no circumstances be understood as denying them. On the other hand, the existence of spiritual qualities ought equally to be understood as not being a bar to the study of those things which can be investigated by science.

If scientific study of language can throw light on human qualities and activities, there is no direction in which there is greater likelihood of illumination than in the investigation of thought, whether that investigation be understood as a part of psychology or a part of logic. It was said earlier that linguists do not deny the existence or importance of mind. The American linguist insists that language entities cannot be profitably investigated in terms of the mental concepts or thought back of them, but this insistence ought always to be understood as carrying with it the corollary that mental concepts can be profitably investigated in terms of the language entities which are so largely instrumental in their formation. It has also been said that language is basic to society. It is therefore probable that increased knowledge of language will mean increased knowledge of society. The promise is already recognized and has already borne fruit, since anthropologists have made brilliant use of linguistic insights. Less broad than thought and society, another area in which linguistic knowledge is beginning to prove useful is in the study of literature, if for no other reason than that literature is an art constructed in language. Similarly, the practical activity of language instruction, whether that of a foreign or the native tongue, can profit by knowledge of the nature of the material which is to be imparted.

I have up to now spoken of the importance of language study from the broad aspect of human knowledge; for the individual student the impact of language study is different. The native language provides its speakers an ever-present and deeply habituated instrument by which they measure and control experience. All adults have had a long indoctrination in the attitude that language is both a transparent glass through which we see the world and a tool by which we would mold it. Therefore the first stages of study of language for the sake of knowledge rather than with a practical aim are apt to be disquieting, or even to seem useless. A somewhat parallel case can be drawn from optics. We think of our eyes as instruments which transmit the "real" appearance of objects directly to our minds. It is often disturbing to realize that our eyes necessarily influence the appearance of objects and that a surface which appears flat to us can scarcely appear so to the nearly spherical eye of a fly. Yet to say that language study is apt to be difficult or disquieting is not the same thing as to say that it is of no value to the individual. An important aim of education is the adjustment of the individual to the world in which he has to live, and linguistic knowledge is a help toward that end. The individual's understanding of reality is increased if he can learn to distinguish the ways in which the structure of his language may influence his perception of reality. Study of language is one of the ways in which a narrow belief in the rightness of one's own ways of doing things, and the wrongness of every other way, can be broken down. It is instructive to find that some languages, even among the European group, are not felt to be inadequate because they do not distinguish between fingers and toes by separate vocabulary items. The knowledge that there are languages which have no tenses at all and others which attach tenses to their nouns is a good introduction to the myriad ways in which men channel the basic human needs, experiences, and activities which indeed remain much the same throughout the world. A student trained in language is aware, on the practical level, of language pitfalls. A very little training may prepare him for failure of communication when an Englishman and an American talk about *corn*. More sophistication is needed for dealing with the situation reported by Bloomfield in which an Englishman misunderstood his American pronunciation of *Comedy Theatre* as a request for a nonexistent *Carmody Theatre*.[4] In all such instances, the student trained in language will deal with the inevitable failure of understanding in realistic terms, without wasting time in denouncing one group or the other for not knowing its own language. And similarly, he is prepared to deal with the difficulties of a foreign language on a more realistic level than by supposing that there is a one-to-one correspondence between its forms and those of English.

By now, I hope that some meaning has been given to the definition of linguistics as the scientific study of language. Linguistics has for its goal the understanding of language, and it is secure in the belief that such understanding will increase human knowledge. It strives to present a picture of language as complete as possible, as consistent as possible, and as simple as possible, again secure in the belief that if these conditions are fulfilled it will be as truly and revealingly a science as is chemistry or astronomy. This book is an attempt to take the reader through some of the

4 *Language,* Holt, New York, 1933, p. 81.

first steps in this young science. The means chosen have been an explanation of the techniques and entities of linguistics in an extended sketch of English, followed by shorter sketches of different language structures. It is not assumed that a sketch of Eskimo will make the reader more capable of finding his way about in Greenland; rather it is hoped that he may gradually come to accept a scientific attitude in a kind of activity where most people, even those thoroughly educated, have not tried to be scientific, and where some, indeed, have resisted the suggestion that they should be. The first stages of investigation and statement may seem to be disturbing and even to introduce confusion where none existed before, but as the design of language and its analysis unfold, clarity emerges, and with it the security of understanding.

C. A Technical Report

The Purity of Commercially Available C14-Labeled Hydrocarbons

M. A. Muhs, E. L. Bastin, and B. E. Gordon

M. A. Muhs and E. L. Bastin are chemists, and B. E. Gordon is a supervisor in radiochemistry at the Emeryville Research Center of Shell Development Company, Emeryville, California. In addition to numerous technical memorandums and reports for internal distribution within the Shell group of companies, the authors have published more than thirty-five papers in professional journals in the fields of polarography, chemical analysis, organic chemistry, and radiochemistry.

Abstract

Gas-liquid radiochromatography (GLRC) has been used to measure the chemical and radiochemical purity of a number of commercially available C14-labeled hydrocarbons. All of the compounds tested had satisfactory chemical purity (>99%) but poor radiochemical purities (0–50%). These results indicate that the purity of any labeled compound from any source should be suspect until it has been properly analyzed.

All of the hydrocarbons found to be radiochemically im-

By special permission of Shell Development Company, Division of Shell Oil Company, and the authors.

pure were successfully purified by preparative scale gas chromatography using GLRC as the test method.

This study suggests that impurities in labeled compounds arise from two sources: first, during the synthesis step which results in traces of impurities of comparable volatility as the parent compound but of higher specific activity; and second, during storage (self-radiolysis) which results in high boiling contaminants (polymers) of specific activity comparable to the parent compound.

This work indicates that analyses for the above impurities should involve (1) GLRC to determine volatile radioactive impurities, and (2) a total activity balance between the injected and the eluted material to determine non-volatile radioactive impurities.

The Purity of
Commercially Available
C¹⁴-Labeled Hydrocarbons
By Gas-Liquid
Radiochromatography

Introduction

In the study of chemical reactions and processes, the use of radioactively labeled compounds is often a valuable technique. So much so, in fact, that in many studies the tracer experiment may be the crucial one. For experimental results to be meaningful and subject to correct interpretations, the labeled compounds must be pure, both chemically and radiochemically.

While conventional methods of analysis such as gas chromatography, infrared and ultraviolet spectroscopy, etc. are adequate in determining chemical purity, they may be inadequate in measuring radiochemical purity. This is because radioactivity to the extent of millions of counts per minute involves quantities of materials of 10^{-7} to 10^{-9} grams. Thus, a compound may be $>99.9\%$ chemically pure and yet have low radiochemical purity. In addition, labeled organic compounds may also contain radioactive impurities of higher molecular weight that arise from self-radiolysis. These are usually non-volatile and do not emerge from a gas chromatographic column. Hence, they are not detected directly.

With the advent of gas-liquid radiochromatography (GLRC),[1, 2, 5]* the determination of radiochemical purity was changed from a tedious and often impossible procedure to a rapid, convenient one for many labeled organic compounds. GLRC is the combination of conventional gas chromatography with radioactive assay. This allows a measurement of the mass and radioactivity of each component as it emerges from the gas chromatographic column. In this way traces of materials of high specific activity which would not produce an observable mass peak can be detected from their radioactivity peak. In addition, since the total radioactivity of the emerging materials can be measured, any difference between this value and the amount injected must be due to non-volatile radioactive impurities providing no decomposition occurs.

We have combined a conventional gas chromatographic apparatus with a Cary high temperature ionization chamber [6, 7] for our GLRC work. This apparatus has been thoroughly described by Nelson, Ressler and Hawes.[7] The apparatus has worked satisfactorily and has been applied to the analysis of commercially available C^{14}-labeled hydrocarbons. This report describes the results of these analyses.

Results

The C^{14}-labeled hydrocarbons tested were in the C_{11} to C_{15} range and were obtained from Company A and Company B. Original specific activities were nominally in the 0.25 to 2.5 mc/mM range. The samples were diluted with pure unlabeled material, before testing, to specific activities in the 0.03 to 0.3 mc/mM range. In addi-

* See Bibliography.

tion to analyses by GLRC, the radioactivity of the diluted samples was measured by liquid scintillation counting. The results of our radioactivity analyses are summarized in *Table 1*. In addition, it should be noted that for all samples the chemical purity as determined by mass peaks of the gas chromatographic curves was 99% or better.

TABLE 1 | **Radiochemical Purity of Commercial C^{14}-Labeled Hydrocarbons**

Hydrocarbon	Stated[a] Activity, μc	Total Activity by Scintillation Counting, μc	Total Activity by GLRC, μc	Activity of Pure Compound Present by GLRC, μc
n-Undecane-1-C^{14}	100	82	53	44
n-Dodecane-1-C^{14} (I)	230	331	248	22
n-Dodecane-1-C^{14} (II)	270	269	252	143
n-Dodecane-1-C^{14} (III)	500	500	426	238
n-Tridecane-1-C^{14}	100	68	53	51
n-Tetradecane-1-C^{14}	100	62	53	44
n-Pentadecane-1-C^{14}	100	80	34	25
1-Dodecene-1-C^{14}	100	16	2.4	0.08

[a] By the supplier.

Three samples of n-dodecane-1-C^{14} were tested. Samples I and II were neat samples from two different preparations while sample III was a benzene solution of material from the same preparation as sample II.

The second column in *Table 1* lists the total radioactivity that should have been in the samples (i.e., the amount ordered) and this can be compared with the actual total activity in the samples as determined by scintillation counting (third column). Tests on our procedure for transferring the samples as received from their containers indicated that at least 99.9% of the activity was transferred and hence no loss occurred during this operation. These data indicate that with all the compounds except the n-dodecane-1-C^{14} samples, the total radioactivity received was 16–82% of that ordered. Two of the n-dodecane-1-C^{14} samples had the correct total radioactivity and one contained appreciably more than indicated on the label.

The fourth column lists the total radioactivity of the samples determined by GLRC. This represents the radioactivity in materials sufficiently volatile to pass through the gas chromatographic column. The difference between this value and that obtained by scintillation counting is a measure of the non-volatile radioactive impurities. All the compounds analyzed showed such impurities and the amounts present in the labeled paraffins range from 6 to 57% of the total radioactivity. With the 1-dodecene-1-C^{14}, 85% of the total radioactivity was in the non-volatile impurities.

The final column lists the amount of radioactivity in the compound of interest. The difference between this value and the radioactivity determined by GLRC is a measure of the volatile (with regard to GC) radioactive impurities. These impurities account for 3 to 97% of the total radioactivity of the volatiles. Some indication of the types and amounts of these impurities can be obtained from a study of *Table 6* in the Appendix. In addition, *Figures 1, 3, and 5* illustrate typical GLRC curves of these materials. From these curves it can be seen that the impurities produce no or very small mass peaks, yet can be readily observed and often identified from their radioactivity peaks. It is for this detection and identification of traces of impurities of high specific activity that GLRC is particularly valuable.

A comparison of the second and last columns of figures in *Table 1* indicates that only 10 to 53% of the radioactivity was found in the paraffins ordered. In all cases the desired material was present in a mixture of other radioactive materials—both volatile and non-volatile. With the olefinic sample essentially none (0.08%) of the radioactivity was in the 1-dodecene.

Two samples of n-dodecane-1-C^{14} (II and III) were reported to have come from the same preparation, but (III) had been dissolved in benzene before shipment in order to reduce self-radiolysis. Our analysis of these materials indicated that they were quite similar with regard to volatile components (see *Table 2*). However, in the benzene solution (III) 15% of the radioactivity was present in non-volatile impurities while this value for (II) was 6%.

For most of the samples, the specific activities of the volatile impurities could be calculated. The weight percent of the impurities was determined from the mass peaks of the GLRC curves, and

TABLE 2 | **GLRC Analysis of n-Dodecane-1-C¹⁴ Samples**

Components	RELATIVE ACTIVITIES, %	
	II	*III*
n-Dodecane-1-C¹⁴	56.8	55.9
Impurity A	0.1	0.2
Impurity B	0.3	2.0
Impurity C	42.8	41.9

their radioactivities were determined from the radioactivity peaks. In some cases no mass peaks could be detected but, for purposes of calculation, values of 0.1%w were assumed (the detectability limit varied from 0.1–0.5%w). The results of these calculations are summarized in *Table 6* in the Appendix.

In order to get a frame of reference for comparison of these data, recall that a specific activity of 1 mc/mM (the nominal value for the original samples) is equivalent to 5 μc/mg for a material with a molecular weight of 200. In addition, the theoretical maximum value for the specific activity of any material with 100% carbon-14 in one carbon atom is 64.5 mc/mM.[4] This maximum value in terms of μc/mg as a function of molecular weight is listed below:

MOL WT	MAX POSSIBLE SPEC. ACT., μC/MG
150	436
200	327
250	262
300	218

With the above values in mind, we can see that the specific activities of the impurities listed in *Table 6* fall over a wide range of values. Some are less, some are about the same, and some are greater than the nominal value of 5 μc/mg that was expected in the original materials. It should also be pointed out that none of the high values exceeds the theoretical limit for compounds in this molecular weight range.

Two samples of n-dodecane-1-C¹⁴ (II and III) and the n-tetradecane-1-C¹⁴ were purified using preparative scale gas chromatography. The purified materials were trapped with 80–90%

efficiency and had chemical and radiochemical purities greater than 99.9% as determined by GLRC and liquid scintillation counting. The specific activities of the desired component in the original products (GLRC) agree well with those of the purified compound (GLRC and scintillation counting) as is shown in *Table 3*.

TABLE 3 | **Specific Activities before and after Purification**

Sample	Desired Component in Impure Sample (GLRC)	Specific Activity, $\mu c/\mu 1$	
		PURIFIED MATERIAL	
		GLRC	Liquid Scint. Counting
n-Dodecane-1-C^{14} (II)	0.264	0.273	0.264
n-Dodecane-1-C^{14} (III)	0.134a	0.130	0.132
n-Tetradecane-1-C^{14}	0.0462	0.0465	0.0459

a Value for the pure n-dodecane-1-C^{14} in the original solution was 1.789 $\mu c/\mu 1$. Before purification this material was diluted to 13.3 times its original volume with inactive material. (1.789) (1/13.3) = 0.134 $\mu c/\mu 1$.

During the gas chromatographic separation of materials there always exists the possibility of decomposition of the sample, which could lead to extra peaks and erroneous indications of the presence of impurities. However, in this work there is no evidence for any decomposition. The impurities detected are real. Paraffins in the presence of an inert atmosphere are very stable in the 200–300° temperature range used in these studies. Decomposition would lead to extra early peaks and in most of the samples studied the impurities were seen as later emerging peaks. Further evidence against decomposition is obtained from the GLRC studies on the purified n-dodecane-1-C^{14} and n-tetradecane-1-C^{14} samples. Only one mass and one radioactivity peak was obtained and the activity emerging from the column (by GLRC) agreed well with the activity of the injected sample (by liquid scintillation counting), as is shown in *Table 4*.

Discussion and Conclusions

The results of this work indicate that commercially prepared labeled compounds contain significant amounts of radioactive

TABLE 4 | **Activity Balance During GLRC
of Purified Labeled Hydrocarbons**

	TOTAL ACTIVITY, μc	
Sample	*Injected*	*Emerging*
n-Dodecane-1-C^{14} (II)	1.53	1.54
n-Dodecane-1-C^{14} (III)	0.818	0.805
n-Tetradecane-1-C^{14}	0.239	0.241

impurities, amounts which may well invalidate experiments in which they are used.

One may speculate, with some confidence, on the origin of these impurities. These are present in two forms, volatile materials of specific activity often far higher than the parent compound and non-volatile impurities. The first source probably arises during the synthesis step wherein the labeled compound is made in milligram quantities. At this point, both the desired and undesirable components are present in comparable specific activity (on a molar basis). Then, after some inadequate purification step, the product is diluted with chemically pure, non-radioactive material (the desired compound). This, of course, drastically reduces the specific activity of the desired compound but leaves the contaminant present in trace amounts but of unaltered specific activity. Hence, the presence of such peaks as shown by the GLRC radioactivity trace. This is not merely an assumption since private conversations with all of the commercial suppliers revealed that this is indeed a common practice.

The second type of impurity, namely the non-volatile material, may also arise during the synthesis step. However, a more common cause is the self radiolysis which goes on during storage. For hydrocarbons one of the common products of such radiolysis is polymer of specific activity comparable to that of the parent compound.

In any case, the findings in this report are unequivocal and the moral is clear: the purity of all radioactive compounds [is] suspect until their radio-chemical purity can be established by a highly efficient analytical procedure such as GLRC. To date there has been essentially no discussion in the literature about possible contaminants in labeled materials. Exceptions are in the paper by Popjak, Lowe and Moore[8] and a statement made by Gordon,[3] where experiences similar to ours are described. These indications plus our findings lead one to wonder about conclusions drawn from many past radio-tracer experiments.

Now, with GLRC, workers in the field of organic tracers (as well as conscientious commercial suppliers) can and should test the purity of many labeled compounds. Before a tracer is used, there should be no evidence of volatile impurities from the GLRC curves, and to insure the absence of any non-volatile radioactive impurities the activity of the injected sample should agree with activity of the eluted sample as calculated from the GLRC curve. Finally, if purification is necessary it can generally be readily accomplished using preparative scale gas chromatography.

We have not investigated the problems involved in establishing the radiochemical purity of labeled compounds too heavy or too unstable to be tested by GLRC. In such cases other chromatographic procedures may suggest themselves but since these methods generally are of lower resolving power than gas chromatography, we can only assume the problems will be formidable.

Bibliography

1. J. P. Adloff, "Chromatography Reviews," M. Lederer, ed., Volume IV, Elsevier, New York, 1962, pp. 19–25.
2. F. Cacace, Nucleonics *19*, No. 5, 45 (1961).
3. B. E. Gordon, in discussion of paper by P. Y. Geng and T. W. Greenlee, "Tritium in the Physical and Biological Sciences," Volume II, International Atomic Energy Agency, Vienna, 1962, pp. 18, 19.
4. S. Kinsman, Radiological Health Handbook, Public Health Service, U.S. Department of Health, Education and Welfare, Cincinnati, Ohio, 1957.
5. R. J. Kokes, H. Tobin, and P. H. Emmet, J. Am. Chem. Soc. *77* 5860 (1955).
6. D. C. Nelson and D. L. Paull, Anal. Chem., *35*, 1571 (1963).
7. D. C. Nelson, P. C. Ressler, and R. C. Hawes, Anal. Chem., *35* 1574 (1963).
8. G. Popjak, A. E. Lowe, and D. Moore, "Advances in Tracer Methodology," S. Rothchild, ed., Volume I, Plenum Press, New York, 1963, p. 127.

Appendix

Experimental
    Apparatus
    Compounds Tested
    GLRC Operating Conditions
    Autoprep Operating Conditions
    Radioactivity Calibration and Calculations
    GLRC Results
    Scintillation Counting Procedure

Experimental

APPARATUS

For the GLRC studies a Wilkin's Aerograph gas chromatography apparatus was connected via a heated tube to a Cary high temperature ionization chamber.[7] The current generated in the ion chamber by the radioactive samples was measured with a Cary

Model 31 vibrating reed electrometer.[7] The outputs of the thermal conductivity detector and of the electrometer were fed to a dual pen "Servoriter" recorder (Texas Instruments, Incorporated) which recorded mass and radioactivity peaks simultaneously.

Purification was accomplished using a Wilkin's Autoprep A-700.

COMPOUNDS TESTED

The eight samples tested are listed in *Table 5* along with their source, identifying designation, activity as designated on the label and as found by scintillation counting. In all cases but one, the samples had been washed out of the sample vial and diluted with the corresponding pure inactive material. Tests on the n-pentadecane-1-C^{14} sample indicated that with such a technique 99.9% of the radioactivity was removed from the original sample vial. The diluted solutions had specific activities ranging from 0.05 to 0.5 $\mu c/\mu l$ and 2 to 6 μl of samples were used for the GLRC analyses.

TABLE 5 | **Compounds Tested**

Compounds	*Source*	*Designation*	TOTAL ACTIVITY, μC	
			Label	*Scint. Count.*
n-Undecane-1-C^{14}	Company A	12-17-63	100	82
n-Dodecane-1-C^{14} (I)	Company B	35-136-2-5	230	325
n-Dodecane-1-C^{14} (II)	Company B	144-27-1	270	269
n-Dodecane-1-C^{14} (III)	Company B	144-27-2	500	500
n-Tridecane-1-C^{14}	Company A	12-24-63	100	68
n-Tetradecane-1-C^{14}	Company A	12-63	100	62
n-Pentadecane-1-C^{14}	Company A	12-16-63	100	80
1-Dodecene-1-C^{14}	Company A	12-16-63	100	16

Three samples of n-dodecane-1-C^{14} were tested. Samples I and II were different batches of neat material and sample III was stated to be from the same batch as sample II only it was diluted in benzene (reported to be 106.5 mg in 1.5 ml). This sample was tested as received without any addition of inactive n-dodecane.

GLRC OPERATING CONDITIONS

Separations were made using a $12' \times \frac{1}{4}''$ column of 30%w SF-96 silicone oil on 60/80 mesh Chromosorb W. For all samples except the n-pentadecane-1-C^{14} the column and detector temperature was about 195°, the injector temperature was 250° and the outlet temperature was 265°. With the n-pentadecane-1-C^{14} the operating temperatures were: column and detector, 245°; injector, 280°; and outlet, 290°. In all cases the temperature of the line connecting the GC outlet to the ion chamber was 280° and the ion chamber oven was held at 300–310°. The current through the thermal conductivity cell was 250 ma. Helium flow rate at the G. C. outlet ranged from 75 to 100 ml/min and the total gas flow rate (helium plus argon) at the ion chamber outlet was 495–503 ml/min (outlet temperature 23°). Recorder chart speed was 3″/min.

Accurate measurement of the absolute radioactivity from GLRC data requires that the amount of sample injected be known accurately. In this work a 10 μl Hamilton syringe was used to inject the sample. The whole sample was drawn into the glass barrel of the syringe and its volume observed. After injection any sample remaining in the needle was drawn into the syringe barrel and its volume measured. The difference of these two volumes represented the volume of the sample injected and was accurate to 0.1 μl.

AUTOPREP OPERATING CONDITIONS

Two n-dodecane-1-C^{14} samples (II and III) and n-tetradecane-1-C^{14} were purified by passage through the Autoprep. A $20' \times \frac{3}{8}''$ column containing 30%w of SF-96 silicone oil on 42/60 mesh GC-22 firebrick was used at 240° with a helium flow rate of 100 ml/min. Other temperatures were: injector 250°, detector 300°, and collector 275°. The detector current was 150 ma. Sample sizes ranged from 0.5–0.7 ml and the material emerging under the principal mass peak was collected in 5 ml spiral traps that were cooled in an ice slurry. Trapping efficiencies ranged from 80–92%.

RADIOACTIVITY CALIBRATION
AND CALCULATIONS

Radioactivity calculations were made in the manner described by Nelson and Paull,[6] and the basic equation used is:

$$N = MED$$

where: N = disintegrations/sec
M = constant, including the ion chamber efficiency, dis. sec^{-1} volt^{-1}
E = max voltage observed for peak, volts
D = correction factor for peak spreading

As shown by Nelson and Paull[6] D is a function of t_1, the mass peak width at half height and K, the ratio of the gas flow rate through the ion chamber to the volume of the ion chamber. To obtain K one can either correct the gas flow for the temperature of the ion chamber or observe the voltage decay of the radioactive peak after the mass peak has essentially disappeared. Nelson and Paull[6] favored the latter technique but we found more consistent results when flow rate was corrected for temperature. The values of K used in this study ranged from 3.49 to 3.57.

The value of M was determined by making measurements on a series of injections of 2-methylundecane-1-C^{14} of known specific activity and which was known to have a chemical and radiochemical purity of better than 99.9%. The average value of M from four determinations with the above standard was 9.50×10^3 dis sec^{-1} volt^{-1} (relative standard deviation $\pm 2\%$) which corresponds to an ion chamber efficiency of 39% for C^{14}. This agrees well with the value of 40% reported by Nelson and Paull.[6]

GLRC RESULTS

Table 6 presents the retention time data for the compounds studied along with relative sizes of the mass and radioactive peaks and the total radioactivity of the complete sample as observed by GLRC. In *Figures 1, 2, 3, 4, 5* are shown tracings of the GLRC curves for the original n-dodecane-1-C^{14} (II), n-tetradecane-1-C^{14} and 1-dodecene-1-C^{14} as well as the curves obtained from the purified n-dodecane-1-C^{14} (II) and n-tetradecane-1-C^{14}.

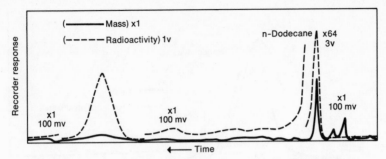

Figure 1. GLRC curve of impure n-Dodecane-1-C¹⁴ (II).

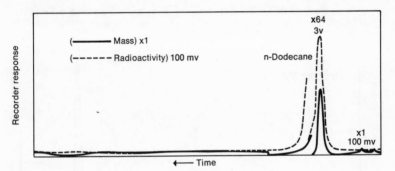

Figure 2. GLRC curve of purified n-Dodecane-1-C¹⁴ (II).

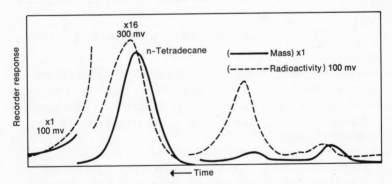

Figure 3. Portion of GLRC curve (3–11 minutes) of impure n-Tetradecane-1-C¹⁴.

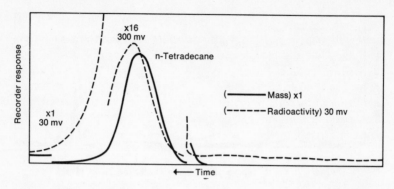

Figure 4. Portion of GLRC curve (3–11 minutes) of purified n-Tetradecane-1-C14.

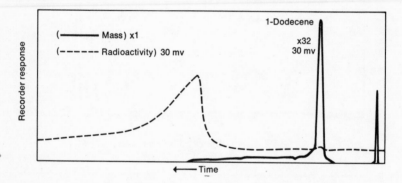

Figure 5. GLRC curve of impure 1-Dodecene-1-C14.

The compounds listed in the tentative identification column are estimated from retention time data and are meant only to give a rough idea of the impurities present. However, in each case the retention time of the main mass peak was checked with that of an authentic sample.

SCINTILLATION COUNTING PROCEDURE

A Packard Tri-Carb automatic liquid scintillation counter was used. The material to be counted was placed in a counting vial with 20 ml of counting solution (6 g 2,5-diphenyloxazole and 0.1

g 1,4-di-[2-(4-methyl-5-phenyloxazoyl)]-benzene diluted to 1 liter with toluene). It was assumed that no quenching occurred with the 1-μl samples used. This small volume of sample was conveniently and accurately measured using 1 μl calibrated capillary tubes ("Microcaps," Drummond Scientific Company, Broomall, Pennsylvania). After being filled the tubes were dropped into the counting solution and the sample rapidly diffused into the solution.

TABLE 6 | GLRC Data

Commercial Samples	G. C. CONDITIONS		SAMPLE			COMPONENTS			
	Column Temp, °C	He Flow Rate, ml/min	Total Wt, mg	Total Activity GLRC μc	tr, min	% Present Normalized		Spec. Activity, μc/mg	Tentative Identification
						Mass	Radio-activity		
n-Undecane-1-C14	195	75	371	53	3.8	>99.5	84	0.12	n-Undecane
					13.3	<0.5	16	23a	n-Pentadecane, tr = 15.3 min
n-Dodecane-1-C14 (I)	195	93	492	248	4.2	98.9	9.0	0.05	n-Dodecane
					16.2	<0.2	24.5	134a	} >n-Tetradecane
					21.4	1.1	66.5	31	
n-Dodecane-1-C14 (II)	195	75	408	252	5.2	>99	56.8	0.35	n-Dodecane
					13.7	<0.2	0.1	0.62a	} n-Pentadecane, tr = 15.3 min
					20.0	<0.2	0.3	1.85a	
					27.7	0.5	42.8	53	>n-Tetradecane
n-Dodecane-1-C14 (III)	195	93	1110	426	0.6	91	0	—	Benzene
					4.3	9	55.8	2.38	n-Dodecane
					10.8	—	0.2	—	
					16.2	—	2.1	—	} >n-Tetradecane
					21.5	—	41.9	—	

Compound								Impurity
n-Tridecane-1-C^{14}	197	75	394	53	0.4	<1	0	—
					1.3	<1	0	—
					2.3	<1	0	4.1[a]	n-Undecane
					3.8	<1	3	0.1	n-Tridecane
					7.7	<99	97	—
n-Tetradecane-1-C^{14}	195	93	735	53	4.1	0.4	1.9	0.3	n-Dodecane
					5.9	0.2	13.4	4.8	n-Tridecane
					8.5	99.4	84.7	0.06	n-Tetradecane
n-Pentadecane-1-C^{14}	245	100	770	34	0.2	0.4	0	—	—
					0.5	<0.1	0	—	—
					0.8	0.3	0	—	—
					1.2	0.1	0.4	0.2	n-Undecane
					2.3	<0.1	1.0	0.4[a]	n-Tridecane
					3.9	99.2	73.2	0.03	n-Pentadecane
					6.7	<0.1	5.7	2.5[a]	n-Heptadecane
					0.1	<0.1	19.8	8.7[a]	n-Octadecane
1-Dodecene-1-C^{14}	192	75	474	2.4	5.2	>99.8	3.4	0.0002	1-Dodecene
					16.3	<0.2	96.6	4.9[a]	n-Pentadecane, tr = 15.3 min
n-Dodecane-1-C^{14} (II) (purified)	195	75	—	—	5.2	>99.9	>99.9	—	n-Dodecane
n-Dodecane-1-C^{14} (III) (purified)	195	93	—	—	4.2	>99.9	>99.9	—	n-Dodecane
n-Tetradecane-1-C^{14} (purified)	195	93	—	—	8.7	>99.9	>99.9	—	n-Tetradecane

[a] These specific activities calculated assuming impurity present at 0.1% w level.

Bibliography

Adler, Mortimer J. *How to Read a Book.* New York: Simon and Schuster, 1940.

Albaugh, Ralph M. *ENGLISH, A Dictionary of Grammar and Structure.* San Francisco: Chandler, 1964.

American College Dictionary, The. New York: Random House, 1966.

Ayer, A. J. "What Is Communication?" in *Studies in Communication.* London: Secker & Warburg, 1955, pp. 23–24.

Baker, Sheridan. *The Complete Stylist.* New York: Crowell, 1966.

Beardsley, Monroe C. *Thinking Straight.* 3rd ed. Englewood Cliffs, N.J.: Prentice-Hall, 1966.

Bernstein, Theodore M. *The Careful Writer.* New York: Atheneum, 1965.

Beveridge, W. I. B. *The Art of Scientific Investigation.* New York: Norton, 1950, 1957.

Bragg, William. *An Introduction to Crystal Analysis.* London: Bell, 1928.

Brookes, B. C. "The Teaching of English to Scientists and Engineers," in Randolph Quirk and A. H. Smith, eds., *The Teaching of English: Studies in Communication.* London: Secker & Warburg, 1959.

Brown, Frank A., Jr. *Biological Clocks.* Boston: Heath, 1962.

————. "Biological Clocks and the Fiddler Crab," *Scientific American,* 190 (April, 1954), 34–37.

————. "Life's Mysterious Clocks," *Saturday Evening Post,* 233 (December 24, 1960), 18–19, 43–44.

————. "Living Clocks," *Science,* 130 (December 4, 1959), 1535–1544.

————. "Responses of the Planarian, Dugesia, and the Protozoan, Paramecium, to Very Weak Horizontal Magnetic Fields," *Biological Bulletin,* 123 (October, 1962), 264–281.

Campbell, Walter S. *Writing: Advice and Devices.* Garden City, N.Y.: Doubleday, 1950.

————. *Writing Non-Fiction.* Boston: The Writer, 1949.

Carr, Edward Hallett. *What Is History?* New York: Knopf, 1965, pp. 32–33.

Darwin, Charles. *The Origin of Species.* New York: Modern Library, 1936.

Darwin, Francis, ed. *The Life and Letters of Charles Darwin.* New York: Appleton, 1889.

Dean, Leonard F., and Kenneth G. Wilson. *Essays on Language and Usage*. New York: Oxford University Press, 1963.

De Voto, Bernard. "What Counts Is the Job," in A. S. Burack, ed., *The Writer's Handbook*. Boston: The Writer, 1959, p. 55.

Evans, Bergen. "But What's a Dictionary For?" *Atlantic Monthly* (May, 1962), pp. 57–62.

Evans, Bergen, and Cornelia Evans. *A Dictionary of Contemporary American Usage*. New York: Random House, 1957.

Follett, Wilson. *Modern American Usage, A Guide*. New York: Hill and Wang, 1966.

Fowler, H. W. *A Dictionary of Modern English Usage*. London: Oxford University Press, 1926.

General Electric's Answer to . . . FOUR WHY'S. Schenectady, N.Y.: General Electric Company, 1958.

Gowers, Ernest. Fowler's *Modern English Usage*. New York: Oxford University Press, 1965.

Gross, Gerald. *Editors on Editing*. New York: Universal Library, 1962.

Gunning, Robert. *The Technique of Clear Writing*. New York: McGraw-Hill, 1952.

Haldane, J. B. S. *A Banned Broadcast and Other Essays*. London: Chatto & Windus, 1946.

Halverson, John, and Mason Cooley. *Principles of Writing*. New York: Macmillan, 1965.

Harker, Janet E. Personal communication, March 28, 1965.

Hathaway, Baxter. *Writing Mature Prose*. New York: Ronald, 1951.

Hazelwood, Jim. "A Beetle Seen REALLY Close," *Oakland* (California) *Tribune,* December 2, 1966.

Hebb, D. O., and Dalbir Bindra. "Scientific Writing and the General Problem of Communication," *The American Psychologist,* 7 (October, 1952), 569–573.

Henn, T. R. *Science in Writing*. New York: Macmillan, 1961.

Hill, Archibald A. *Introduction to Linguistic Structures*. New York: Harcourt, Brace & World, 1958.

Hook, J. N. *Hook's Guide to Good Writing*. New York: Ronald, 1962.

Hoover, Herbert. *Memoirs of Herbert Hoover,* Vol. I: *Years of Adventure*. New York: Macmillan, 1951.

Hund, Walter J. Personal communication, December 1945.

Jordan, John E. *Using Rhetoric*. New York: Harper & Row, 1965.

Kane, Thomas S., and Leonard J. Peters. *A Practical Rhetoric of Expository Prose*. New York: Oxford University Press, 1966.

Kapp, Reginald O. *The Presentation of Technical Information*. New York: Macmillan, 1960.

Kent, George. "Hottest Job on Earth," *Reader's Digest,* 90 (January, 1967), 184–189.

Keyes, Langley Carleton. "Profits in Prose," *Harvard Business Review,*
39 (January–February, 1961), 105–112.

Klare, George R. *The Measurement of Readability.* Ames: Iowa
State University Press, 1963.

Lewis, G. N., and Merle Randall. *Thermodynamics and the Free
Energy of Chemical Substances.* New York: McGraw-Hill,
1923; rev. 1961.

Lewis, Norman. *The Comprehensive Word Guide.* Garden City, N.Y.:
Doubleday, 1958.

————, ed. *The New Roget's Thesaurus in Dictionary Form.* Garden
City, N.Y.: Doubleday, 1961.

Martin, Harold C., and Richard M. Ohmann. *The Logic and Rhetoric
of Exposition.* New York: Holt, Rinehart and Winston, 1963.

Merrill, Paul W. "The Principles of Poor Writing," *Scientific Monthly,*
LXIV (January, 1947), 72–74.

Muhs, M. A., E. L. Bastin, and B. E. Gordon. *Purity of Commercially
Available C^{14}-Labeled Hydrocarbons.* Emeryville, Calif.: Shell
Development Company, 1964.

Newsome, Verna L., and Enola Borgh. *Sentence Craft.* New York:
Macmillan, 1952.

Ogden, C. K., and I. A. Richards. *The Meaning of Meaning: A Study
of the Influence of Language upon Thought and of the Science
of Symbolism.* New York: Harcourt, Brace & World, 1962.

Parrish, Wayland Maxfield. "Prose Rhythm," in *Reading Aloud.* New
York: Ronald, 1953.

Pence, R. W., and D. W. Emery. *A Grammar of Present-Day English.* 2nd ed. New York: Macmillan, 1963.

Quiller-Couch, Arthur. *On the Art of Writing.* New York: Putnam,
1916.

Reynolds, Paul R. *The Writing and Selling of Non-Fiction.* Garden
City, N.Y.: Doubleday, 1963.

Shurter, Robert L. "Let's Take the Strait Jacket off Technical Style,"
Mechanical Engineering, 74 (August, 1952), 664.

Snow, Sir Charles P. *The Two Cultures: And a Second Look.* London:
Cambridge University Press, 1963.

Souther, James W. "What Management Wants in the Technical Report," *Journal of Engineering Education,* 52 (April, 1962),
498–503.

Sporn, Philip. *Foundations of Engineering.* New York: Pergamon,
1964.

Standard Periodicals Directory. New York: Oxbridge, 1964–1965.

Stevenson, Robert Louis. "On Some Technical Aspects of Style in Literature," in Lane Cooper, ed., *The Art of the Writer* (Ithaca,
N.Y.: Cornell University Press, 1952), p. 320.

Strunk, William, Jr., and E. B. White. *The Elements of Style.* New York: Macmillan, 1959.

Talbot, L. "Energy Sources and Energy Conversion," in John R. Whinnery, ed., *The World of Engineering.* New York: McGraw-Hill, 1965.

Terracini, Emma D., and Frank A. Brown, Jr. "Periodisms in Mouse 'Spontaneous' Activity Synchronized with Major Geophysical Cycles," *Physiological Zoology,* XXV (January, 1962), 27–37.

Tichy, H. J. "Engineers Can Write Better," *Chemical Engineering Progress,* 50 (February, 1954), 104–107.

Walcutt, Charles Child. *An Anatomy of Prose.* New York: Macmillan, 1962.

Ward, Ritchie R., "Readability of Technical Writing," *Proceedings, 14th International Communications Conference,* Society of Technical Writers and Publishers, Chicago (May, 1967), p. 32.

Webster's New Collegiate Dictionary. Springfield, Mass.: Merriam.

Webster's New World Dictionary. New York: World.

Webster's Third New International Dictionary, Unabridged. Springfield, Mass.: Merriam, 1964.

Weisman, Herman M. *Basic Technical Writing.* Columbus, Ohio: Merrill, 1962.

What to Report. Pittsburgh: Westinghouse Electric Corporation, 1962.

Willis, Hulon. *Structure, Style, Usage: A Guide to Expository Writing.* New York: Holt, Rinehart and Winston, 1964.

Wilson, Kenneth G., R. H. Hendrickson, and Peter Alan Taylor. *Harbrace Guide to Dictionaries.* New York: Harcourt, Brace & World, 1963.

Woodford, F. Peter. "Sounder Thinking Through Clearer Writing," *Science,* 156 (May, 1967), 743–745.

Index

A NOTE ON THE TYPE

The text of this book was set on the linotype in a face called TIMES ROMAN, designed by Stanley Morison for *The Times* (London), and first introduced by that newspaper in 1932.

Among typographers and designers of the twentieth century, Stanley Morison has been a strong forming influence, as typographical adviser to the English Monotype Corporation, as a director of two distinguished English publishing houses, and as a writer of sensibility, erudition, and keen practical sense.

Composed, printed, and bound by American Book–Stratford Press, Inc.

Design by LEON BOLOGNESE